O9-CFS-541

STANFORD UNIVERSITY LIBRARIES

WITHDRAWN

1/22/00

a history of communications

Designed and produced
by Erik Nitsche

THE NEW ILLUSTRATED LIBRARY OF SCIENCE AND INVENTION

1 *a history of rockets and space*
2 *a history of ships and seafarin*
3 *a history of flight*
4 *a history of weaponry*
5 *a history of astronomy*
6 *a history of electricity*
7 *a history of land transportatio*
8 *a history of physics*
9 *a history of communications*
10 *a history of chemistry*
11 *a history of the machine*
12 *a history of medicine*

Hawthorn Books Inc.
Publishers, New York

MAURICE FABRE   VOL. 9 | a history of communications

All rights reserved, including the right
to reproduce this book, or portions thereof,
in any form, except for the inclusion of brief
quotations in a review. All inquiries
should be addressed to Hawthorn Books, Inc.,
70 Fifth Avenue, New York City 11.
This book was designed and produced by
Erik Nitsche International, S.A., Geneva.
It was printed and bound in Switzerland
by Heliogravure Centrale, Lausanne.
The engravings were made by
Heliogravure Centrale, Lausanne.
The text paper is white gravure 140 gr/m².
This book is published simultaneously
in Canada by McClelland & Stewart, Ltd.,
25 Hollinger Road, Toronto 16.
The Library of Congress has catalogued
this volume of The New Illustrated Library
of Science and Invention
under card number 63-10478. Suggested
decimal classification for this series is 500.

First edition · October, 1963
H-4540

Adapted from the French
by Peter Chaitin

contents

introduction 6

1 *in the beginning was the word 9*

2 *the art of writing 23*

3 *books, paper, and printing 39*

4 *the rise of the press 55*

5 *communications through space 65*

6 *"what's past is prologue" 85*

chronology 106

credits 111

Man is a social being. He congregates in groups, and builds families, cities, and nations, and the mainspring of these institutions, and of all human institutions, is communication between man and man. Man seeks out his own, either for the waging of war or for the exchange of goods and ideas. Even in societies, such as monasteries, which applaud the solitary virtues the process of communication is a constant factor, if only through the study of books, in which one generation speaks to another.

In a broad sense the history of man is the history of communications. Harold A. Innis, the Canadian scholar, goes so far as to insist that every major change in the methods of communication has been followed by a major change in the structure of society. The introduction of movable type hastened the collapse of feudal institutions; the development of the popular press and of the telegraph and telephone brought on the large-scale democratization of society. Today, perhaps, the era of television and of Telstar signals the approach of a global civilization. One might argue in this connection whether or not the horse precedes the cart or the chicken the egg; but in any case it is not communications in the broadest sense that is our primary concern in this volume, but rather the simple development of communications from the first meaningful "ugh" of prehistoric man to the latest method of teaching by electronic machine.

It is a paradox of our time that man has built a vast network of communications in a variety of media, and yet with all the techniques and technology at his disposal has not yet really learned to communicate in the fullest sense with

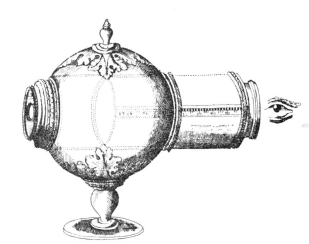

others. A so-called "hot-line" for the instant transmission of vitally urgent messages between the White House and the Kremlin has been recently inaugurated. The hope is that in the event of a crisis in international relations the leaders of the United States and of the Soviet Union would be able to reach a hurried agreement to avert war. That such a device is possible is a tribute to our capability; but that it should be necessary speaks volumes about our inability to communicate.

Even if the ultimate failure—atomic war— does not occur, many of the dangers of our times will still be with us. Some commentators on the human condition see a bleak future for man, in which all the means of modern mass communications will be harnessed by a ruling elite to deprive the individual of his freedom and his privacy. In his novel *1984*, the British writer George Orwell sketched just such a picture. Drawing heavily on the experience of Nazi Germany and Soviet Russia, and sensing many authoritarian tendencies in more democratic countries, he predicted a world of misery and poverty in which man would be "conditioned" to accept and even to glory in his wretched state. Certain pessimists see something like Orwell's nightmare vision on the way. They conceive of modern man as being bogged down in a welter of over-persuasive communications, his individuality lost through his eagerness to forget himself in the artificial world of mass entertainment. They believe that mankind is becoming too pliant and complacent, that he is being lulled into a more or less permanent state of semi-consciousness; a creature whose leisure time is spent in front of a television screen.

Yet there are many indications that man will not end as he began, in a state of blissful ignorance. If he is reading, watching, and listening to more trash than ever before, he is also buying more classical records and serious literature than at any time in history. If the tension of our times has caused many to turn to the mass media as a soporific, it has turned others toward an active participation in public affairs.

Most of all, mass communications have freed the ignorant and enslaved from their heritage of passive acceptance by giving them a vision of what the world should be. An idea is no longer something that slowly spreads by word of mouth; today it leaps across the world in a matter of seconds. Freedom and justice are no longer concepts limited to a lucky few; and even if these ideas are sometimes imperfectly understood, the worldwide impulse to liberty represents a great victory for Western civilization. Nowhere was this impulse more dramatically illustrated than in Hungary in 1956, when a people rose in an effort to throw off oppression. Without the ability of mass communications media to cross borders and spread the idea of freedom, hope would be gone for millions.

Yet there is hardly cause to be sanguine. If radio, television, films, newspapers, and the like have liberated mankind from abysmal ignorance, superstition, and hopelessness, they have not yet served to educate him fully. Whether they do or not is essentially up to man himself, for all forms of communications, from speech to television, are only tools to be used for humanity's ends. The individual is the prime mover. What the ancients knew is still true: "Man is the measure of all things."

4   Archers in combat—a prehistoric attempt
to "tell a story." These neolithic paintings
were discovered deep in the Sahara in 1956.

To communicate is to be alive, to be active, in relation with others. Helen Keller, deaf, dumb, and blind as an infant, lived at the lowest physical level until she was able to break through to the outer world. For communication is essentially an interchange, a question and a reply, an action and a reaction between an individual and the environment in which he lives. As everyone knows, communication in this sense is not confined to man but is shared to a certain extent with insects and animals. It may involve sight, touch, and hearing, gestures, expressions, and noises. But only man has developed that highly organized means of communication we call language, and his ability to use the spoken word to further his own purposes has had a lot to do with his dominant position on this globe.

"In the beginning was the word." Although man has always recognized and revered the power of language, other means of communication have been at his disposal—a gamut of gestures, a wide range of facial expressions, dances, and pictures designed to convey meanings in series; but since the beginning of human society language has been man's most powerful tool in conveying his thought, in giving form to his activity, in formulating his hopes and plans for the future, and in preserving his memory of the useful past. Language and society have grown up together; as the one grew more complex, so did the other. And no wonder, for they are different aspects of the same thing. Language is a form of social behavior, both expressing and at the same time giving shape to the beliefs and attitudes of people in groups —whether families, social classes, villages, tribes, or nations.

5-8   These paintings by the aborigines of Australia's Northern Province—one of the rare cases in which "primitive art" has not been subjected to undue outside influence—offer an interesting comparison with prehistoric art. Fishing and hunting scenes (5-6) reflect the aborigine's daily life and his concept of the animals around him. His more mystical experiences are exhibited in the paintings which show the pursuit of the evil spirit (7) and of the sea turtle (8). Mimi spirits, timid and peaceful creatures of the rocks, surround the latter. Hiding in caves, they are seen only by children.

9-11 *Aztec figures from a mid-19th century work on the dactylology of the ancient Mexicans are supposed to illustrate the author's theory of the existence of a primitive hand language among the Aztecs. The figures show the words "to favor" and "alliance" (9), "virgin" and "wife" (10), and "to choose" and "protector" (11). Rather similar figures were used in the primitive "picture writing" employed by the Aztec and the Maya.*

Considering the importance of language in the development of human society, it is astonishing to find how little is known about its origins. Writing, which by definition is a lasting record, occurred quite late in human history, but speech, which is by nature evanescent, may have arisen tens of thousands of years before writing first appeared. Who knows what language, if any, was spoken by paleolithic man—he whose bones, whose tools, whose paintings on the walls of caves have survived, but not his speech? The absence of any real evidence for the origin of human speech has opened the subject up to endless speculation. There were always those, of course, who held that speech was divinely revealed to man, a gift from God. Others, more logical but no less wide of the mark—including Democritus, Locke, Condillac, and Adam Smith —held that speech was adopted by mankind in convention; in other words, that it might be looked upon as an artificial creation legislated, so to speak, into existence.

From the nineteenth century onward, research into the origin of speech increased in quantity, seriousness, and intensity—but the results were as meager as ever. Among recent scholars several alternative theories have arisen and have been given colorful names which should not detract from their serious intent. There is, for instance, the "bow-wow" theory, which holds that human words first arose from imitations of natural sounds such as the barking of a dog. Or the "pooh-pooh" theory, that speech began with exclamations of fear, pain, pleasure, and the like, and its close relative, the "yo-he-ho" theory, that it started with grunts of physical exertion, or the "sing-song" theory, holding

that primitive chants opened the way to speech. The Soviet scholar Marr considers that articulate speech began as an accompaniment to communication by gesture. And he bases all variations and combinations in subsequent speech on only four primitive sounds originally used with these gestures—sol, ber, yon, and rok. Other linguists believe that speech appears only when, as with children, a person's mental activity attains a certain level of development.

All of this admirable scholarship does little to clarify the actual origin of language. In fact, most of it is just as speculative as the persistent legend that the first and original language was the "language of the birds." This bizarre idea crops up among the ancient Egyptians, among the Incas of South America, and in the stories of Orpheus, Siegfried, and St. Francis of Assisi. It was quite seriously discussed by the medieval alchemist Fulcanelli, who wrote, "Those rare writers who have spoken of the 'language of the birds' accord it first place in the origins of speech. They say that it goes back to Adam, who used it to impose under God's will suitable names designed to define the characteristics of the people and things of creation."

The idea that there must have been *some* original language is as persistent as the legend of the "language of the birds." Up to the end of the seventeenth century, Hebrew, the language of divine revelation, was held to be the original language of humanity. Leibnitz protested vigorously against this view, and gradually emphasis shifted from a search for the single original language to the fact, which was becoming increasingly obvious, that there were groups, or families, of languages. In attempting to unravel

the relationships that linked the various tongues scholars began to develop a new tool for the study of the origin and diffusion of languages. Historical and comparative linguistics, especially as applied to the problem of the Indo-European group of languages in the nineteenth century, began to provide a far sounder and more scientific basis for the study of language in general.

Years of careful and devoted scholarship have built up a picture of the world's languages, living and dead, which is almost frightening in its complexity. It is estimated that at the present time there are some 3,000 languages currently in use. In Europe alone scholars count 120. Then there are the dead languages, including Sumerian, Sanskrit, Avestan, Latin, Phoenician, Scythian, Iberian, and the rest. Altogether, it seems that almost 4,000 languages have disappeared during the course of human, and thus lingual, evolution. A strange example is the Etruscan, which can be read because it was written in a Greek script, but understood very little or not at all because its syntax differs from that of every known language.

And all these languages, living and dead—except for a few, such as the Baswue and the Japanese Ainu, which so far have defied classification—are complexly interrelated, through common origins, similar structure, word roots, and word sounds, thus falling into family groups, and subdivisions of these groups, some enormous, some quite insignificant. The largest overall groupings are the African, Semitic-Hamitic, Indo-European, Sino-Tibetan, Japanese-Korean, Ural-Altaic, Austronesian, North American Indian, and South American Indian.

To these, many other groups and subgroups may be added ad infinitum: the Caucasian, the Dravidian, the Finno-Ugrian, 26 smaller families from North America, including Eskimo, Algonquin, Uto-Aztec and Iroquois, 20 from Central America including Mayan and Zapotecan, and 77 from South America and the West Indies, including Arawak, Carib, and Chibcha. The count for the Americas may not be very exact, for the classification of the numerous Indian languages is still in an embryonic state.

Of these so-called "families" of languages, some may be spoken by mere thousands of people, whereas the Sino-Tibetan languages of southeastern Asia are spoken by well over 600 million people, and the Indo-Iranian languages by some 400 million. Yet the latter is merely one subgroup of the great Indo-European, or Aryan, family of languages, which includes numerous other subgroups, such as the Germanic, Romance, Slavic, and lesser units like the Greek, Albanian, and Armenian.

The Indo-European family of languages, now used by about half of the world's population, is supposed to have stemmed from a small, compact area—variously located from the Iranian plateau through Central Europe to the Baltic—whose inhabitants migrated south and westwards before 2000 B.C., spreading the basic structure of their language to many diverse areas. Much later, Latin, a minor Indo-European dialect centered near the mouth of the Tiber River, spread by conquest over most of Europe and the Mediterranean. Offshoots of Latin and of the Germanic subgroup of the Indo-European family—French, Spanish, and English—have

12 *Aztec symbols from the Borgia Codex. The Aztec and Mayan writing of pre-Columbian Central America is not far removed from primitive picture writing: human figures, snakes, weapons, pyramids, and other readily identifiable objects appear in these decorative but crude scripts. Although most of the Aztec and nearly all of the Mayan manuscripts were destroyed after the Spanish conquest, scholars have made some progress in deciphering parts of those which remain. They deal mostly with mathematical, astronomical, and chronological records. The Russians in particular, using electronic computer techniques, have made important progress towards the decipherment of some of the more important Mayan codices.*

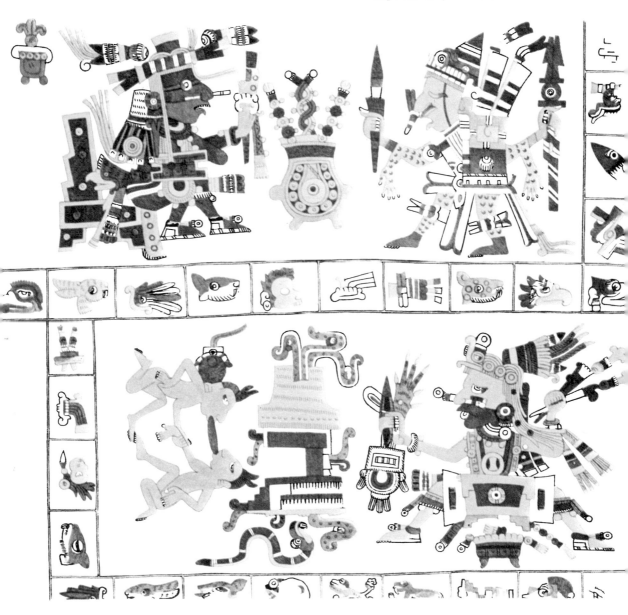

now travelled around the world. Yet the close relationship of the many widespread branches of the Indo-European is nevertheless still quite clear. Travellers to Iran, for instance, are astonished to find that such basic words as "mother" and "father" are almost the same as in English.

Such a picture of languages and language groups growing and dying, evolving, splitting, competing, ever active and ever changing, seems utterly confusing until it is remembered that language is merely an expression of human society. Languages, like cultures, nations, civilizations, tend to disintegrate into local groupings unless there is a strong centralizing influence to enforce unity and growth. The Romans spread Latin around the known world, but when the Roman Empire broke up, Latin, too, diverged into the various Romance languages we know today. Languages follow social, political, economic, and religious trends. Dying languages, for instance, have been revived for political reasons—as in Ireland and Israel. Even within a given language area, differences in dialect, usage, and vocabulary will reflect the fine shadings of class differences, of the differences between young and old, and between one profession and another. Language is indeed a form of social behavior.

It is for this reason that all attempts to create an artificial "universal" language have met with failure, despite the persistence of many inventors who seemed to have believed that language could be imposed on society, like laws. There is a record of a certain Arab, Sheik Mohyi-ed-Din, who invented a language called "bala balan." The enterprising John Wilkins, Bishop of Chester, published a grammar and dictionary of a language of his invention in 1668. Towards 1887 a Pole, Zamenhof, introduced the better-known Esperanto, of which Ido is a refinement. In 1925 Occidental was created. Then came Interlingua and Gala, the latter formulated on the basis of the most recent of linguistic data.

All of these efforts merely illustrate the blindness of many scholars to the historical aspects of language. From earliest times language not only reflected the growth and change of human society in all its complexity, but played an even more positive role in shaping society and in building up that accretion of ways of doing things, beliefs, and knowledge we call human culture—or, in a higher manifestation, civilization. Before the invention of writing, and in the absence of written history, the accumulated lore, learning, and wisdom of the group was handed down from one generation to another by word of mouth. The spoken and remembered word *was* history. Without writing tools, speech had to serve; and without archives there was the retentive memory of certain men.

The oral tradition of prehistoric times remains a closed book to us. With the rise of civilization it was both supplanted and destroyed by literature, which etymologically means "written thing"—the narrator becoming a poet or scribe. But in reading early epics, such as the *Iliad* and *Odyssey* (presumably written down by Homer about 800 B.C.), we are afforded at least a glimpse into that vast unwritten reservoir of tales, legends, myths, and heroic precepts which lay behind them and which were probably based upon Sumerian, Phoenician, or Egyptian originals. In fact all of antiquity

13 Figures from the Aztec
Telleriano Codex. Although they took
the idea of writing from the Maya,
the Aztecs did not improve upon
the Mayan script. Their own writing
tends to be over-elaborate, unlike the more
delicate and restrained Mayan script.
In a sense, the Central American writing
reflects the nature of the "semi-
civilization" which arose there: some
studies, such as mathematics and
astronomy, were quite advanced, and yet
the Central American people ignored
the use of the wheel, metal tools, and
domestic animals. Whereas writing was
an integral part of the developing
civilizations of the ancient Near East,
the Aztec and Mayan writing never
achieved more than occasional phonetic
values, was not utilitarian.

reverberates with tales told and retold by anonymous voices. There were the Hebrew narrators, whose histories and exhortations were later incorporated in the Old Testament. There were Celtic bards, Anglo-Saxon scops, and Scandinavian scalds. Undoubtedly the last great keepers of the ancient oral tradition in Western civilization were the medieval German minnesingers, and the troubadours and trouvères of France who wandered from castle to castle singing of chivalry and love, the one in langue d'oc, the other in langue d'oïl.

An even closer intimation of how it must have been to live without the written word is furnished by the study of primitive peoples of more recent times. In innumerable tales, verses, fables, legends, and myths they give their answer to those three timeless questions asked by the painter, Paul Gauguin, at the bottom of one of his paintings. Where do we come from? What are we? Where are we going? But the remembered lore of the primitive is not confined to tales of the creation and of how to please the gods, but also aims to guide the hearer through the crises and requirements of daily life—birth, death, marriage, hunting, or the harvest.

Naturally, only a gifted specialist, a man trained in the intricacies of traditional lore, can be entrusted with the task of passing on such knowledge. In Polynesia, verbal transmission was carefully regulated and attained an astonishing degree of accuracy, and the itinerant professional reciters faced an audience that was in no sense passive, but participated and responded. Melanesians considered the word as of supreme importance, and identified not only

14

the speaker but themselves with its importance, so that there were precise techniques not only for speaking but for preparing to speak. Genealogies, prayers, myths, poems, songs, and legends were the property of the reciters—the harepo of Tahiti, the tuhuna of the Marquesas Islands, the rogorogo of the Gambier Islands— who were trained by the priests and had to pass examinations, especially in the retentiveness of their memories, before they were allowed to instruct the next generation in the adventures of the great gods, Atea, Tane, Tu, Rongo, Oro, and Taaroa, the creator of the world.

Among the North American Indians, knowledge and transmission of the sacred texts was in the hands of the priests, or shamans. In common with other primitive societies, the Indians distinguished between myths, which were considered true, and tales, which were fantasies containing simple moral precepts for children to memorize. Myths, for instance, often told the story of the Great Ancestor—the coyote of the Columbia-Fraser plateau, the raven of the northwest Pacific coast, or the god Widapoki of the southwest. While Indian shamans were trained to impart these myths and tales by word of mouth, the shamans of the Eskimo, steeped in magic and fantasy, had as one of their chief functions the preservation and passing on of magic formulas used for a variety of purposes— to cure sickness, to ensure successful hunting, and so forth.

In Africa, too, the spoken word has been of central importance in preserving and handing down the myths and precepts of the many primitive cultures found there. Almost 250,000 different African tales have been counted by one spe-

cialist. Indeed, it has often been said that primitive Africa has a "spoken civilization." In this type of society one may still occasionally find a "master of speech" attached to a king or tribal chieftain. Traditionally, the "master of speech" was a kind of walking file with his head crammed full of information about his people and their relations with their neighbors, past and present. He acted as librarian, notary public, and historian all at once, and like the shaman or professional reciter often displayed incredible feats of memory. Such keepers of the oral tradition were of crucial importance to primitive society, but with writing and civilization their function has all but disappeared. And we are the losers.

Both primitive and prehistoric men were without writing; but did they have any other means of transmitting ideas aside from speech? Certainly the rock paintings from the Neolithic period discovered recently in the Sahara region, as well as similar paintings by more recent primitives, seem to be close to "telling a story," which after all means communication.

And then there are the older paleolithic cave paintings from France and Spain which, taken as a whole, may also represent an effort to tell a story, as well as certain markings upon artifacts from the same era—possibly indicating ownership. Until the creation of writing, however, direct speech was the chief method of communication. But slowly man was groping his way towards new means which would enable him not only to set down that which he learned but to pass it along to others in a more accurate fashion. But this comes close to the next subject, the origin of writing.

*14   A tom-tom, or drum, made in the
shape of an ox. Used by primitive people
all over the world, tribal drums were
often employed as a very early form
of telegraph, relaying messages through
the forests and jungles. Drums of
various kinds were also of great
importance in the social and religious
life of the primitives, who danced,
marched to war, and invoked their
gods to the insistent beating of drums.
15   A sand painting by the Navajo Indians
of North America tells a "creation"
story concerning a beggar boy who was
picked up by a mother eagle and placed
in the nest with the eaglets. Primitive
peoples, living as they do in such close
proximity to the animal world, inevitably
give animals an important place
in their myths and legends.*

15

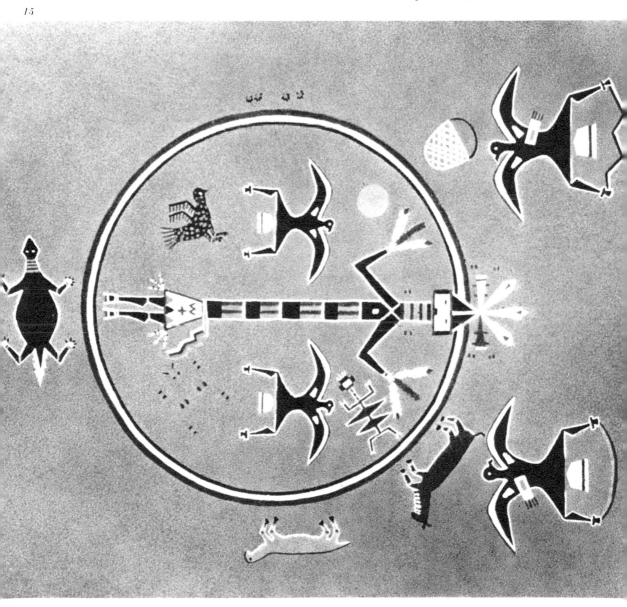

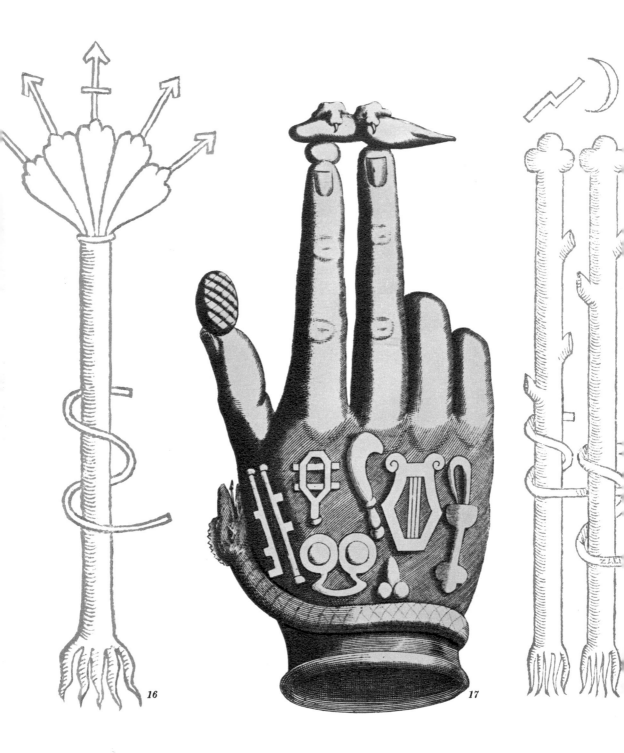

16   17

16-19 *Astrological symbols for mercury (16) and other metals (18), from "Preciosa Margarita," published in Venice in 1546, and a charm to ward off illness and other woes, found in a Roman tomb (17, 19). In man's efforts to understand the nature of the universe and his own fate, he has often sought answers in superstition and in "false sciences." Astrology, one of the oldest of the "false sciences," fostered in its believers (and still does foster) a sense of intimate communication and influence between the heavenly bodies and the earth. Thus the sun, moon, and planets were associated from earliest times not only with individual metals, but also with specific organs of the human body.*

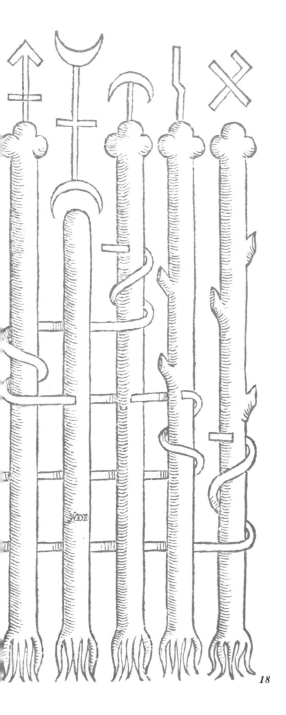

18

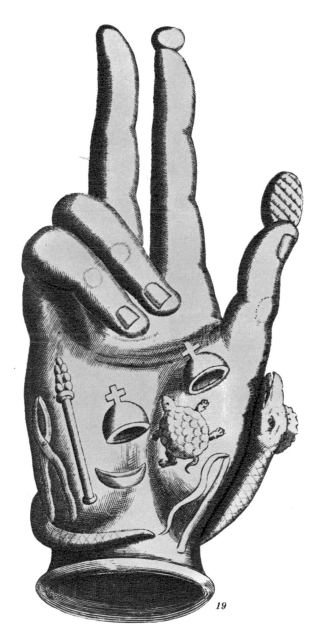

19

20 Babylonian cuneiform writing, about 600 B.C. Wedge-shaped letters were usually impressed in wet clay.
21 Babylonian clay cylinder of the sixth century B.C.
22 (Next page.) Detail from the famous law code inscribed on a stele by Hammurabi of Babylon about 1800 B.C.

Writing is the memory of the ages of man. Within its signs, symbols, ideograms, pictograms, and letters lies his intellectual heritage. It is also the record of man's thought, for to write, man is forced to think in a logical manner. Writing, again, is the key to the future, for that which was written yesterday and today will give to posterity the means with which to build new worlds upon the basis of the old. If man suddenly lost his power of speech, he would still be able to learn from the past, communicate in the present, and pass on knowledge to the future—through the medium of the written word. But if he were to lose his ability to read and write, he would soon find himself in a time vacuum. The exchange of information would depend entirely upon speech and those audio-visual devices which are mere supplements to the written word. Without writing, those skills, sciences, arts, philosophies, and bodies of laws and customs which man has perfected over the centuries would perish, and succeeding generations would be bereft of historical guides. Man would be forced to retrace his steps on the long and painful road to civilization.

This is not to say that society is impossible without writing. For much the greater period of humanity's existence there was no writing at all. But pre-literate societies were extremely rudimentary. Even today, many peoples exist without writing, and their pre-literate condition is reflected in the primitiveness of their lives. But once writing came into existence, urbanization became possible, as well as highly developed forms of trade, government, law, religion, literature and the systematized growth of knowledge. It is small wonder that the ancients

21

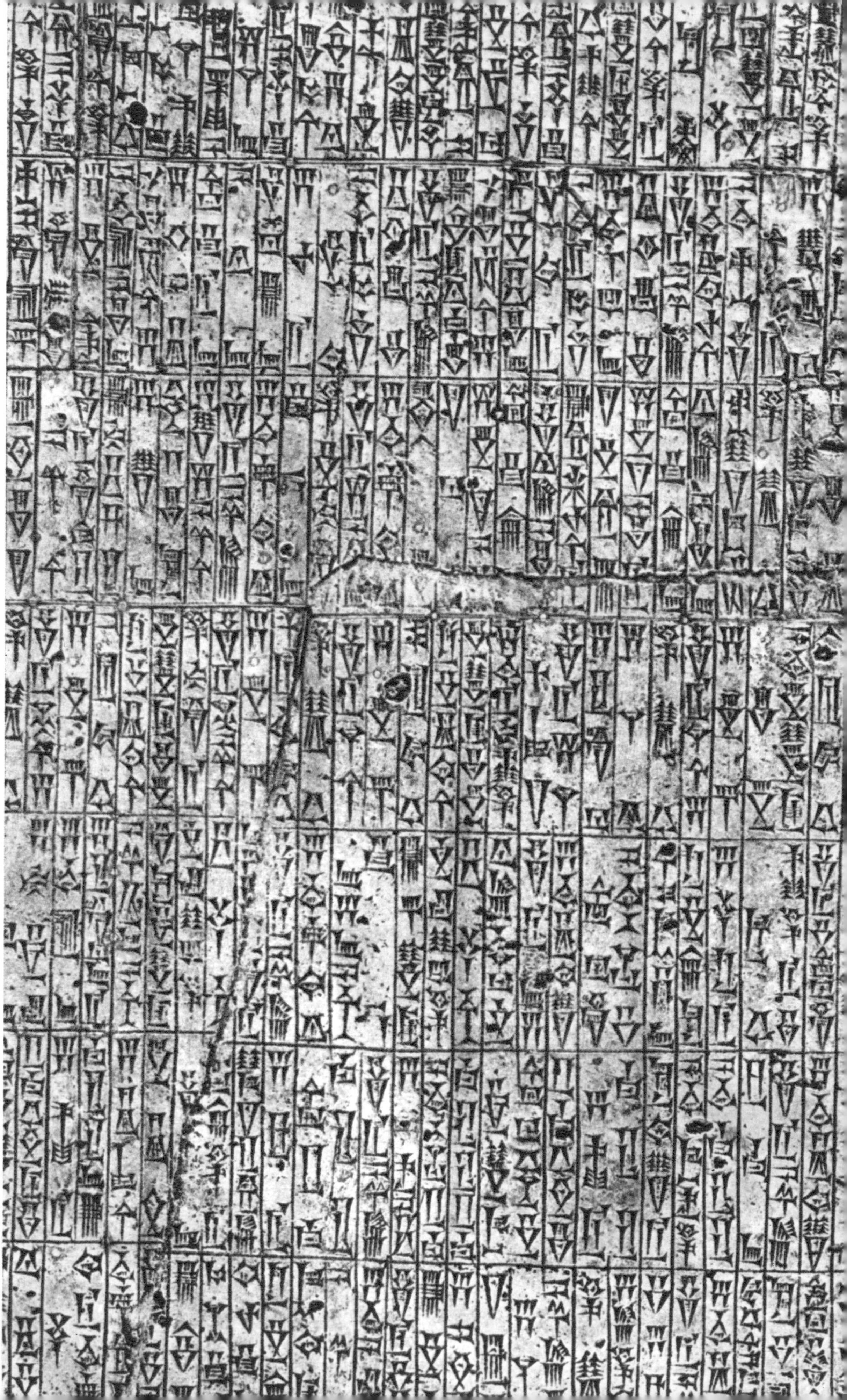

22

often regarded writing as divine in origin; in fact in some societies certain types of script were reserved for sacred purposes. The Egyptians believed that Thoth, god of wisdom, invented writing; the Babylonians credited it to Nebo, god of destiny, learning, and science; and the Greeks sometimes talked of Hermes as the father of the art.

Yet writing did not suddenly appear fully developed, a tool ready for all the complex tasks now assigned to it. In its growth many different methods were tried. Most of these eventually disappeared while a few continued to develop into those types of script that now exist. Even today there is little unity. Various kinds of writing are now in use which bear little resemblance to one another. One has only to glance at the Western alphabets and compare them with Chinese characters to discover that there is no relationship between them, although both have served as the basis of highly complex cultures. But the characteristics of each script have played a large part in determining the nature and growth of the two civilizations. The simplicity and flexibility of our alphabetic system has helped create a fast-paced world of movement and material progress, while the complexity and static nature of Chinese script was reflected for thousands of years in the formal, tradition-bound, serene life of the Celestial Empire.

Fully developed writing consists of converting sounds, words, or concepts into visual symbols and marking them down in an orderly sequence to convey ideas. This is a highly sophisticated procedure, and thousands of years passed before man took the first hesitant steps toward such a goal. Not until the fourth millennium B.C. did there appear a systematized effort to transcribe ideas into script. It is true that as early as 20,000 B.C. man was drawing images on the walls of his caves—the cave paintings of Altamira in Spain, for instance, date back to that time. But this is at best pre-writing, not a conscious rendering of ideas, and was probably bound up with ritual magic—perhaps a sympathetic device to insure a good hunt. In no way can the cave paintings be called writing. The famous Altamira bison merely tells the viewer that an artist of the Upper Paleolithic period drew the portrait for purposes upon which we can only speculate.

Despite the non-literate character of the cave paintings they do hold an important place in the history of writing, for it is likely that from them came the first attempts to string together a series of pictorial representations of objects—pictograms—to convey thought. When this happened an early form of writing had come into existence.

Before going into pictography and its various successors, it would be well to examine briefly other precursors of writing. Most of these forms were in one way or another mnemonic (memory-aid) devices. Such aids exist even in our own day: when a man ties a piece of string around his finger to remind himself to buy a quart of milk, he is using a mnemonic aid very similar to those employed by his prehistoric ancestors. An example of the use of knots in keeping a record of numbers was related by Herodotus. Darius, a Persian king, gave his Ionian commanders a strap of 60 knots and told them, "Men of Ionia... every day undo one of the knots, beginning on

23 *Egyptian hieroglyphics carved in wood, from the Third Dynasty. The first known Egyptian hieroglyphic writing dates from the beginning of the third millennium, B.C. Like Egyptian civilization itself, hieroglyphic reached full development as early as the First Dynasty. Later it gave birth to two forms of popular cursive writing, the demotic and the hieratic. Despite the efforts of scholars from the sixth century onwards, hieroglyphic remained a mystery until the discovery of the famed Rosetta stone by one of Napoleon's officers in 1799. Comparing the three inscriptions on the stone—in hieroglyphic, demotic, and Greek—the Frenchman Jean-François Champollion and other scholars finally deciphered this highly stylized script.*

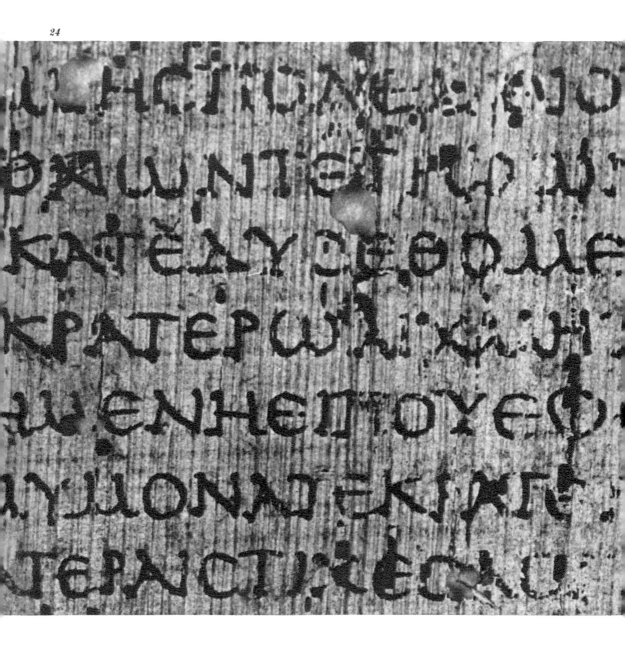

24 An example of Greek script from
the third century B.C., written with
a reed on papyrus. The alphabet,
invented by the Semites, was brought to
Greece by the Phoenician mariners in
the ninth or tenth century B.C. and
was so greatly improved that it has
been only slightly changed during the
subsequent three thousand years of
its existence. All European alphabets
stem from the Greek. The earliest
writing, like that of the Egyptians,
read from right to left, and was only
succeeded by the left to right style
in the fifth century B.C. In the inter-
mediate "boustrophedon" system, lines
read alternately from right to left
and then from left to right.

25 A "classic" Greek inscription carved
in stone, from the first century A.D.

25

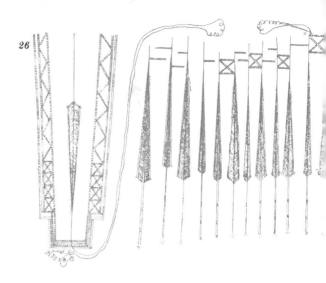

the day on which you see me start my march against the Scythians. Should I fail to return before all the knots have given out, you are at liberty to sail home . . . ."

Knotting has not only been used to aid the memory and record numbers, but also to convey information. The Peruvian *quipus*—a collection of threads of different sizes and colors—when knotted in certain ways were used to relate news and disseminate decrees. Similarly, the wampum belt of certain American Indian tribes was often used for sending messages or recording events. The famous Penn wampum belt of 1682 shows two figures hand in hand—one an Indian and the other a white man (who can be identified by his hat). The belt commemorates the treaty of peace between William Penn, leader of the white settlers of Pennsylvania, and the Delaware Indians. But for all their usefulness, mnemonic devices are very primitive forms of communication. They had little direct bearing on the development of writing.

The earliest known pictographic writing is called cuneiform, a name derived from the wedge-shaped script that eventually characterized it. Although it came into general use throughout the Middle East, cuneiform is usually credited to the Sumerians, a people who moved into southern Mesopotamia during the fourth millennium B.C. Whether the Sumerians actually invented the script or merely adopted it is unknown, but before it died out, cuneiform went through several stages of development. In its earliest form it was purely pictographic. A reclining silhouette meant man, a divided triangle woman, a circle the sun, and so on. Its next stage was ideographic. The circle now not

only represented the sun, but also concepts associated with it—heat, day, and time. As in all pictographic and ideographic writing, the pictured image bore no relation to the sound of the spoken word, though this in itself had one great advantage; the written language could be understood by people who spoke mutually unintelligible dialects.

In time, however, cuneiform made a great step forward; the script came to be partly phonetic. (During this period scribes began impressing the characters into wet clay tablets by means of a broad-headed stylus, and the script assumed its characteristic wedge shape.) Some signs came to denote not only an object or a quality, but also the sound associated with that object, thus establishing a definite link between the spoken and the written language. Ideograms, while still in use, could not be completely understood without a knowledge of the phonetic values of the script; hence the mixture of ideographic and phonetic characters led to considerable confusion. Some symbols, called polyphones, had several phonetic values and perhaps some ideographic ones as well, while others (homophones) had closely related sounds but entirely different meanings (for example, "hole" and "whole" in English). A system of determinatives was therefore introduced. These unpronounced symbols, indicating the category to which ambiguous words or sounds belonged, became the key to an understanding of the script.

Near the middle of the third millennium B.C., the Sumerian civilization waned. Cuneiform, by now highly developed, was taken over and spread by the Assyrians, Babylonians, and many

26 *A love-song written on birch bark*
in the script of the Siberian language,
Yukagira, whose affiliations are
virtually unknown. Of the people
living in the Soviet Union today, only
a little over one half are Russian
speaking. The rest speak some 145 other
languages, including various Slavic,
Baltic, Ural-Altaic, Caucasian, and
Indo-European tongues. Up to recent times
many of these could not be written
until alphabets were devised for them.
27   *Letters of a Hebrew alphabet, from*
a woodcut in the very rare "Voyage de
Jean de Mandeville en Orient," printed
by Richel in 1481. First to abandon
the pictographic or ideographic values
of their scripts in favor of a true
phonetic alphabet were the Phoenicians,
Hebrews and other eastern Semites.

27

other peoples of the ancient Near East. By the sixth century B.C. the Persians had adapted it to their Indo-European tongue. They made it much more flexible, created a syllabary of 41 sounds, and came very close to building a true alphabet.

The decipherment of cuneiform—to the point where it has been deciphered, since much remains to be done—was one of the great scholarly achievements of the nineteenth century. From this feat has come knowledge of immensely complex and highly developed cultures, some of which, such as that of Babylon during its great age in the eighteenth century B.C., rivaled classical Greece in their grasp of science and the beauty of their literature. It was in this period that the Babylonians developed a code of justice that closely paralleled Mosaic law. Such a culture depended on a relatively flexible, simple method of writing, as was cuneiform at the height of its glory.

Shortly after the Sumerians began the development of their script, the Egyptians embarked upon the same path. The earliest known examples of hieroglyphics (from the Greek, literally "sacred carving") date back to 3100 B.C., while the latest example to be discovered was inscribed in 394 A.D. The progress of hieroglyphics followed the example of the older script to a remarkable degree. Undoubtedly evolved from pictographic signs, by Old Kingdom times (3400-2475 B.C.) it had developed ideograms, determinatives, and even a system of 24 consonantal signs. Thus the hieroglyphic image of an owl could be used in three distinct ways: to denote the bird itself, the characteristics associated with owls and, finally, the sound "m," for this was the dominant consonant in the

Egyptian word for owl. Unfortunately the Egyptians did not fully realize the advantages of their consonantal system and hence never achieved a true alphabet.

Anyone desiring a government career in Egypt was obliged to be literate; a schoolboy who wished to make a high place for himself in his society was forced to learn more than 700 different characters. The writing of hieroglyphics was also considered an art form. Esthetics were at least as important as clarity of meaning, and no attempt was made to separate words, provide punctuation, or rationalize the flow of the script. All of this was left to the scribe's intuitive sense of beauty. As an art, writing also required a high degree of craftsmanship—something not everyone could attain. Consequently a more cursive script developed, called hieratic. The hieroglyphs were reduced to a bare outline of their original complex forms. Gradually hieratic became the dominant script in law, science, and business, while hieroglyphics came to be used only for religious and official inscriptions. By the seventh century B.C. an even more cursive form evolved, known as demotic (from the Greek, "of the people"), but all three scripts continued to exist side by side. Eventually hieroglyphics were used for monumental inscriptions only, hieratic had become the script for priestly writings, and demotic was reserved for everyday, secular use.

Not until the early nineteenth century was any progress made in the decipherment of Egyptian script. During Napoleon's Egyptian campaign of 1799 the famous Rosetta Stone was discovered. Upon this stone was inscribed a priestly document—drawn up in 196 B.C.—in hieroglyphic,

28-30 *Examples of Egyptian papyri showing hieroglyphic and hieratic characters. The hieroglyphic writing (28, and above the painting in 29) was used mainly for carving official texts into stone. Two forms of cursive writing grew up alongside the formal hieroglyphic, the hieratic, used almost exclusively for sacred texts, and the demotic, used by the layman for everyday purposes. Most Egyptian papyri were written in the hieratic (29, at left, and 30) and the demotic scripts.*

demotic, and Greek. Thanks to the presence of this "bilingual key" the script was deciphered by the French scholar Champollion in 1822, and from the Rosetta Stone has flowed much of our knowledge of the history of ancient Egypt.

While the languages of the Middle East and North Africa were inching their way toward a syllabic script, in the Far East the Chinese were developing a style of writing that to this day has not evolved beyond a combined ideographic-syllabic form. Despite the static character of their written language, the Chinese built a great civilization, partly because their script, clumsy as it was, played a vital role in unifying a vast country with many different spoken dialects and languages. Since China's population numbers some 700 million, and other scripts of the Far East are derived from Chinese writing, it would be well to examine it.

There are some 40,000 separate characters in the Chinese dictionaries, about 8,000 of which are currently in use. For everyday purposes a basic knowledge of 600 to 1,000 characters is all that is needed, but to be truly erudite one must be familiar with at least 3,000 to 5,000. The characters are divided as follows: There are 608 purely pictographic signs. Some abstract ideas are represented by 740 signs, formed by combining the pictograms. Thus the character representing "woman," twice repeated, means "quarrel." Other abstractions are represented by 598 ideograms—for example, the character "heart" indicates thought. Position, number, and the like are expressed by 107 signs, and the meanings of 372 signs change according to the direction in which they are written. The most

important classification, comprising nine-tenths of all Chinese characters, is partly figurative and partly phonetic. For example, the character for "place" is pronounced "li," but when an image of a fish is combined with this sign, the meaning is no longer "place" but "carp," also pronounced "li." Finally there are 187 keys, consisting of one to 17 strokes, used to give characters different meanings. It is significant that the Chinese Communists, in their drive to modernize the nation, have promulgated reforms looking toward the eventual alphabetization of the language. Should this occur, it will be the first really qualitative change in the long history of Chinese script. The same trend exists in Japan, where attempts are being made to replace the existing ideographic-syllabic system with the Latin alphabet.

Before going on to modern Western script, mention should be made of the non-alphabetic writing discovered on Crete, site of the ancient Minoan civilization. The famous English archaeologist Sir Arthur Evans began his diggings in Crete in the late 1890's, and over the decades he uncovered much evidence of a highly developed culture, including several different scripts. Two are linear scripts dating from about 1700 to 1550 B.C., called linear "A" and "B." To date, little progress has been made in deciphering Linear A, but in 1952 Linear B was translated by two Englishmen, Michael Ventris and John Chadwick. Ventris had first made the revolutionary discovery that the language of the script was not Cretan but an archaic form of Greek, thus establishing an early cultural link between Crete and the Mycenaean civilization of the mainland. The decipherment of the

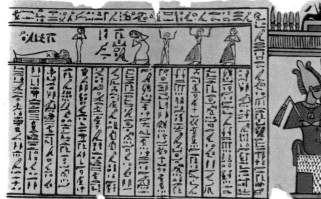

Table of the 214 classifying keys (radicals) with their numbers and French transcription, read in numerical order (right column first, top to bottom).

No.	Clef	Transcription
1	一	yě
2	丨	kouen
3	丶	tchŏu
4	丿	pié
5	乙	yě
6	亅	kiŏue
	Clefs de deux traits	
7	二	eulh
8	亠	theôu
9	人 (亻)	gîn
10	儿	gîn
11	入	gĕ
12	八	pā
13	冂	khiông
14	冖	
15	冫	
16	几	ki
17	凵	
18	刀	tao
19	力	liĕ
20	勹	pao
21	匕	pí
22	匚	fâm
23	匸	hí
24	十	chĕ
25	卜	poŭ
26	卩	tciĕ
27	厂	hàn
28	厶	tçŏu
29	又	yéou
	Clefs de 3 traits	
30	口	khèou
31	囗	youu
32	土	thŏu
33	士	ssé
34	夂	tchi
35	夊	sŏui
36	夕	siĕ
37	大	tá
38	女	niŭu
39	子	tçé
40	宀	mién
41	寸	tçun
42	小	siào
43	尢	váng
44	尸	chī
45	屮	tçào
46	山	chân
47	巛	tchôuen
48	工	kông
49	己	ki
50	巾	kin
51	干	kân
52	幺	yâo
53	广	yèn
54	廴	ín
55	廾	kông
56	弋	ŷ
57	弓	kông
58	彐	kì
59	彡	chân
60	彳	tchi
	Clefs de 4 tr.	
61	心	sîn
62	戈	kō
63	戶	hòu
64	手	cheôu
65	支	tchī
66	攴	pŏu
67	文	vên
68	斗	teôu
69	斤	kin
70	方	fâng
71	无	voû
72	日	jĕ
73	曰	yuĕ
74	月	yoŭe
75	木	mŏu
76	欠	kién
77	止	tchì
78	歹	ya
79	殳	tcheôu
80	毋	moû
81	比	pĭ
82	毛	mào
83	氏	chì
84	气	khì
85	水	chŏui
86	火	hŏ
87	爪	tchao
88	父	fóu
89	爻	yâo
90	爿	pân
91	片	pién
92	牙	yâ
93	牛	nieôu
94	犬	khiuen
	Clefs de 5 tr.	
95	玉	yŏu
96	玄	yuên
97	瓜	coûa
98	瓦	và
99	甘	cân
100	生	sēng
101	用	yong
102	田	thièn
103	疋	pĭ
104	疒	pŏ
105	癶	pŏ
106	白	pĕ
107	皮	pí
108	皿	mîn
109	目	mŏ
110	矛	meôu
111	矢	chì
112	石	chĕ
113	示	chí
114	禸	jŏu
115	禾	hô
116	穴	hiuĕ
117	立	lĭ
	Clefs de 6 tr.	
118	竹	tchŏu
119	米	mì
120	糸	mĕ
121	缶	feôu
122	网	vang
123	羊	yâng
124	羽	yòu
125	老	lào
126	而	eúlh
127	耒	loŭi
128	耳	eùlh
129	聿	yŭ
130	肉	jŏu
131	臣	tchîn
132	自	tçé
133	至	tchì
134	臼	kiéou
135	舌	chĕ
136	舛	tchòuen
137	舟	tcheôu
138	艮	kĕn
139	色	sě
140	艸	tçao
141	虍	hôu
142	虫	tchông
143	血	hiuĕ
144	行	hîng
145	衣	ŷ
146	襾	sié
	Clefs de 7 tr.	
147	見	kién
148	角	kiŏ
149	言	yèn
150	谷	kŏu
151	豆	téou
152	豕	chì
153	豸	tchái
154	貝	pĕi
155	赤	tchĕ
156	走	tçéou
157	足	tçŏ
158	身	chîn
159	車	tchē
160	辛	sîn
161	辰	chîn
162	辵	tchŏ
163	邑	yĕ
164	酉	yéou
165	釆	pién
166	里	lì
	Clefs de 8 et de 9 traits	
167	金	kîn
168	長	tchâng
169	門	moûen
170	阜	feôu
171	隶	taï
172	隹	tchŏu
173	雨	yü
174	青	tsing
175	非	fī
176	面	mién
177	革	kĕ
178	韋	goéi
179	韭	kiéou
180	音	în
181	頁	yĕ
182	風	fông
183	飛	fī
184	食	chĕ
185	首	cheôu
186	香	hiâng
	Clefs depuis 10 traits jusqu'à 17	
187	馬	ma
188	骨	kŏ
189	高	cao
190	髟	pieôu
191	鬥	téou
192	鬯	tchang
193	鬲	liĕ
194	鬼	kuĕi
195	魚	yâ
196	鳥	niao
197	鹵	loû
198	鹿	lŏ
199	麥	mĕ
200	麻	mâ
201	黃	hoâng
202	黍	chŏu
203	黑	Hĕ

*31 Chinese characters; an alphabet from
Diderot's "Encyclopédie." Of the two
principal systems of writing in the world
today, the Western, drawn from the
Semitic phonetic alphabet, has proved
to be the most adaptable and active.
The static Chinese script, still a
pictographic-ideographic system, has had
the effect of restricting the written
language while leaving the spoken language
unrestrained. All Chinese write the same
script, but they speak so many different
dialects that they often have to call
in interpreters to understand one another.
32-43   (Next page.) In a form of vocal
communication antedating the written
sign, Parisian street vendors at the beginning
of the 16th century cry their
wares, ranging from shoes (32) to
alphabets (38), wood (39), and wine (40).*

script was a feat of immeasurable value in adding to our knowledge of the origins of Greek culture.

Alpha and beta, the first two letters in Greek, give us our word "alphabet"—a set of symbols representing the individual sounds of a language. The creation of a true alphabet may be likened to the invention of the wheel, so important was it to the development of Western culture. Its exact origins are a matter of scholarly dispute. This much, however, can be said with a fair degree of certainty; the forerunner of the Graeco-Latin alphabet developed along the narrow Mediterranean strip that now includes areas of Jordan, Israel, Syria, and Lebanon. Sometime between the eighteenth and sixteenth centuries B.C., the breakthrough to something very closely resembling a true alphabet was accomplished. Which group invented it is of little importance, but what does matter is that the coastal Phoenicians carried it to Greece in the tenth or ninth century B.C. There it was adapted and improved upon, and became the basis of all contemporary European scripts.

The major change which the Greeks made was the addition of vowel symbols. This was the final touch, and a true alphabet was now in existence. Not long after the alphabet came to Greece it was adopted by the Etruscans, probably in the eighth century B.C., and from there it went to the Romans, who modified the forms of the letters in adapting it to their own language, and through their conquests spread the alphabet first through Italy and then to Gaul and the rest of southwestern Europe. Meanwhile the Greeks were standardizing their own alphabetic forms; but it was not until the middle of the

fourth century B.C. that a single 24 letter alphabet was in use throughout the country. The Roman alphabet achieved its final form of 23 letters when the conquering Romans, in the first century B.C., adopted the Greek symbols for "Y" and "Z." The later spread of the major alphabets was determined by religion: those states which adhered to the Eastern Orthodox Church used the Cyrillic alphabet, adapted from the Greek, while the alphabet of the Catholic nations was based upon the Latin.

After the Latin alphabet achieved its final form, all that remained was to develop a conventional style of lettering. Writing, both in capital block letters and in cursive script, went through several modifications. The calligraphy of our own day dates from the ninth century, when the Carolingian Frankish Empire was at its height. This in turn had two principal offshoots: the Gothic, a form still used in Germanic countries, and the roman and italic scripts of the Italian Renaissance.

Since the nineteenth century, the Latin alphabet has spread around the globe through the medium of missionaries and colonists. It has been particularly useful in the artificial creation of writing for contemporary peoples who never developed scripts of their own. It has failed to win a place in most of the Far and Middle East; yet it is probable that more people are familiar with the Latin alphabet than with any other form of writing. Its flexibility and simplicity have made it an almost perfect instrument for the dissemination of literacy as well as information and entertainment through books, newspapers, and magazines, subjects which will be discussed in the next two chapters.

souliers vieulx

32

Haren soz   Haren soz

35

33

Aseurete   les bon furés

36

mabelle poiree mes beaus epinars

qui veul de boulesi

34

raue: doulceraue

37

beaulr a b c belles heures

38

Uoirze   Jolis

41

Clos quorus les

39

Argēt mid uict   saigne petit

42

A la malle   tache

40

Jlrbuc de marcs

43

*44   Carrier pigeons as used in Syria, a woodcut from
Richel's incunabulum of Jean de Mandeville's travels in
the Orient, printed in 1481. Before the days of radio
and telegraph homing pigeons, flying perhaps 700 miles in
a day, were prized as an efficient means of communication.*

Books are among the noblest inventions of humanity. Within the pages of the millions of volumes written since the first book was set down lie the hopes and fears, the histories, religions, philosophies and sciences, the foibles and follies, the dreams and triumphs of literate man's sojourn on earth. Books have changed the course of history and have set societies on entirely new paths: consider, for example, the impact of the Bible on Western civilization.

But books and writing are not synonymous. Before books could be perfected, a writing surface had to be developed that was light, not too bulky, and could be easily stored. The first great advance came with the Egyptians' use of the papyrus plant in the third millennium B.C. Lengthwise slices of the plant's stem were placed in two layers at right angles to each other, and pressed together with a glue made from water and the juices of the plant itself, making a material that was flexible, light, and durable. The sheets were fastened together into scrolls, some more than 120 feet long, which could be rolled up for storage. Characters were inscribed by means of a reed soaked in a mixture of water, gum, and lampblack—the earliest known form of ink. Among the most famous of the Egyptian papyri is one entitled *The Book of the Dead*, generally considered the first book, as it is the earliest known work of considerable length that survives today (older papyri representing literature have been found, but in a fragmentary state).

After papyrus came parchment, perfected in the Asia Minor city of Pergamum (from which its name derives) in the second century B.C. Actually, animal skins had long been used as a

leuauerunt anforã inter terram et celũ.
Et dixi ad angelũ qui loquebat ĩ me.
Quo iste deferũt anforã? Et dixit ad
me. Vt edificet ei dom9 ĩ terra sennaar:
et stabiliat et ponat ibi sup basem suã.

Et conuersus sum: et leuaui
oculos meos et vidi: et ecce qua-
tuor quadrige egredietes de medio du-
orũ montiũ: ⁊ motes montes erei. In
quadriga prima equi rufi: in quadriga scda equi nigri in quadriga tercia
equi albi: ⁊ in ꝗdriga quarta equi varij ⁊ fortes. Et respodi: ⁊ dixi ad angelũ qui loquebat in me. Quid sunt hec
dñe mi? Et respondit angelus: et ait
ad me. Isti sunt ꝗtuor venti celi: qui e-
grediũtur ut stent cora dñatore oñis
terre. In qua erãt equi nigri egrediebã-
tur in terrã aquilonis: et albi egressi
sunt post eos: et varij egressi sunt ad
terrã austri. Qui aũt erãt robustissimi
exierũt: ⁊ querebãt ire ⁊ discurrere per o-
mnẽ terrã. Et dixit. Ite: ⁊ perambulate
terrã. Et perambulauerũt terrã. Et vo-
cauit me: ⁊ locut9 est ad me dices. Ecce qui egrediũtur in terrã aquilonis:
requiescere fecerũt spiritũ meũ in terra
aquilonis. Et factũ est verbũ dñi ad
me dicens. Sume a transmigratione
ab oldai et a thobia et ab idaia et ve-
nies tu in die illa et intrabis domũ io-
sye filij sophonie qui venerũt de babi-
lone: ⁊ sumes aurũ ⁊ argentũ ⁊ facies
coronas et pones in capite ihesu filij
iosedech sacerdotis magni: ⁊ loqueris
ad eũ dicens. Hec ait dñs exercituum
dices. Ecce vir: oriens nomẽ eius. Et
subter eũ orietur: et edificabit templũ
dño: et ipe extruet templũ dño. Et ipse
portabit gloriã: ⁊ sedebit ⁊ dñabitur
sup solio suo. Et erit sacerdos sup solio suo: et cõsiliũ pacis erit inter illos
duos. Et corone erũt helem et thobie
et idaie ⁊ hen filio sophonie: memori-
ale in templo dñi. Et qui procul sunt
venient et edificabũt in templo dñi: et
scietis quia dominus exercituum misit me ad vos. Erit aũt hoc: si auditu
audieritis vocẽ dñi dei vestri.

Et factũ est in anno quarto darij
regis: factum est verbum dñi ad
zachariã in quarta mensis noni qui
est casleu. Et miserũt ad domũ dei sa-
rasar et rogomelech et viri qui erãt cũ
eis ad deprecandã faciẽ dñi: ut diceret
sacerdotibz dom9 dñi exercituũ ⁊ ꝓphe-
tis loquẽtes. Nũquid flendũ ē michi
in quinto mense: uel sanctificare me
debeo sicut feci iam multis ãnis? Et
factũ est verbũ dñi exercituũ ad me dicens. Loquere ad omnẽ ꝓplm terre: et
ad sacerdotes dicens. Cũ ieiunaretis
et plangeretis in quinto ⁊ septimo per
hos septuaginta ãnos: nũquid ieiu-
niũ ieiunastis michi? Et cum comedi-
stis ⁊ bibistis: nunꝗd nõ vobis come-
distis et vobismetipsis bibistis? Nũquid nõ hec sunt verba que locutus
est dñs in manu ꝓphetaꝝ prioꝝ cũ ad-
huc iherusalẽ habitaret et esset opulẽ-
ta: ipa ⁊ urbes in circuitu ei9: et ad au-
strũ ⁊ in cãpestribz habitaretur? Et factũ est verbum dñi ad zachariã dices.
Hec ait dñs exercituũ dicens. Iudiciũ
verũ iudicate: et misericordiã et misera-
tiones facite unusquisꝗ cũ fratre suo.
Et viduã et pupillũ ⁊ aduenã et pau-
perem nolite calũniari: ⁊ malũ vir fra-
tri suo non cogitet in corde suo. Et no-
luerũt attendere et auerterunt scapulã
recedẽtes: ⁊ aures suas aggrauauerũt
ne audirent: et cor suum posuerũt ut
adamãtem ne audirẽt legẽ et verba ꝗ
misit dominus exercituũ ĩ spiritu suo

47   Matthias Elzevir, printer of
Leyden, who until 1622 carried
on the business founded by
his father, Louis Elzevir I.
48   Johann Gutenberg (1400?-
1468), inventor of printing from
movable type, about 1450.
49   The woodcut is a technique
close to early printing. From
the "Almanach des Bergers," 1491.
50   A medieval pledge given to
Philippe-Auguste, King of France
from 1165 to 1233, has been
authenticated with many seals.
51   During the Middle Ages
documents were usually "signed"
with a stamp seal which made an
impression such as this.

writing surface in Greece and elsewhere, but
it was in Pergamum that methods were evolved
for the production of a durable, velvet-smooth
parchment, suitable for writing on both sides.
The development of parchment in turn gave
rise to the copying of numerous manuscripts for
the great libraries of the Hellenistic world (although the method of folding parchment into
pages, as in a modern book, did not originate
until about the second century A.D.).

By the first century B.C., the Sosii brothers of
Rome were doing a flourishing trade in the copying and selling of manuscripts. The Romans had
already gone far in developing a publishing and
book distribution system. Authors received
some protection from unauthorized publication
of their works, and the age-old bane of writer
and publisher—censorship—had already appeared. Under the rule of Julius Caesar a system
of public libraries was established, but in general
throughout the ancient world access to books
was, and would continue to be for a long time
to come, the preserve of the very rich. Yet the
libraries that did exist were sometimes incredibly rich storehouses of learning and culture.
Alexandria during its great age (304 to 30 B.C.)
had two royal libraries which contained 490,000
different scrolls, but by 391 A.D. these reposi-
tories of "pagan" learning had been largely
destroyed by the Roman conquerors, an out-
rage for which the overzealous Christian con-
vert Theodosius I was chiefly responsible.

While the West was developing parchment,
the Chinese were perfecting an even more useful
writing material. Almost two centuries before
Christ they reduced silk to a pulp from which they
obtained a very high-grade paper. In 105 A.D.,
one Ts'ai Lun succeeded in turning the husks of
cheaper fibers, such as cotton, into paper pulp.
This practical advance spread throughout
China and then between the seventh and eighth
centuries, to Korea, Japan, and as far west as
Persia. The Arabs, in their sweep through the
Middle East, fell heir to the paper-making process after they captured Samarkand in the
eighth century. But they were slow to pass it
on to the West, and not until the twelfth century
did Arab merchants bring the new "parchment"
to Italy. By that time the Moslems in Spain
had begun to manufacture paper on their own.
It is believed that the first European production
of paper took place in Spain around 1150.
Finally, between the thirteenth and fifteenth
centuries, paper mills were established throughout western Europe—first in Italy, then France,
Germany, England, and Scandinavia.

But to turn back to the history of books: with
the fall of the Roman Empire the secular writing and publishing of books disappeared, and
the Church became the protector and repository
(but not necessarily the disseminator) of knowledge during the Dark Ages that descended on
Europe. Throughout this period the monasteries
had a virtual monopoly in the production and
preservation of books. Many of them had a large
room called a *scriptorium*, where highly skilled
monks would laboriously copy and recopy the
sacred texts as well as historical, literary, and
philosophical writings. The Irish monastic
orders in particular—they existed throughout western Europe—specialized in the copying of manuscripts, and developed, out of the
original Byzantine practice, a beautiful and
highly stylized form of illumination, or the

49

50

51

52-63 Printers' devices from the 15th and 16th centuries: mark of Théodore Borne (52) shows a 15th century printers' shop. Mark of Jacob Dupuy (53), Paris, 1582, and that of Robert Estienne, 1503-1559, "father of French lexicography" (59). The "T.L." press of 16th century Paris (55). Antoine Vérard, printer in Paris, 1485 (56), and Antoine Candidus of Lyon, 1588 (67). Louis Elzevir I (58) founded the famous Dutch press at Leyden near the end of the 16th century. Marks of French printing houses, Jacob Jontus, 1562 (59), the Wechel Press, 1572 (60), Vignon, 1582 (61), Jérémie des Planches, 1583 (62), and the Genevan printer, Gramonet, 1643 (63).

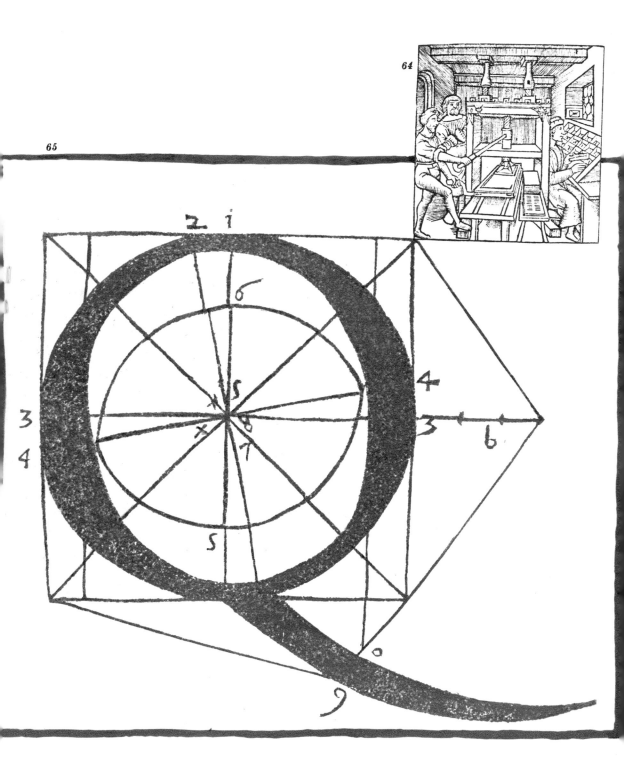

64 A 16th century printers' workshop,
shown in an anonymous woodcut. After the
invention of movable type by Johann Gutenberg
in 1450 printing spread rapidly during
the second half of the century from its home in
southern Germany throughout all of Europe.
This was largely due to the efforts of
the German printers themselves, many of whom
moved from town to town taking their equipment
with them. The 16th century, however, saw
the greatest artistic progress among printers.
By this time they were highly instructed
men and often sought the collaboration
of some of the greatest painters
and printmakers of their time.
65-66 But the art of penmanship lost none
of its finesse, as is shown by these letters
from a late 16th century book on writing.

66

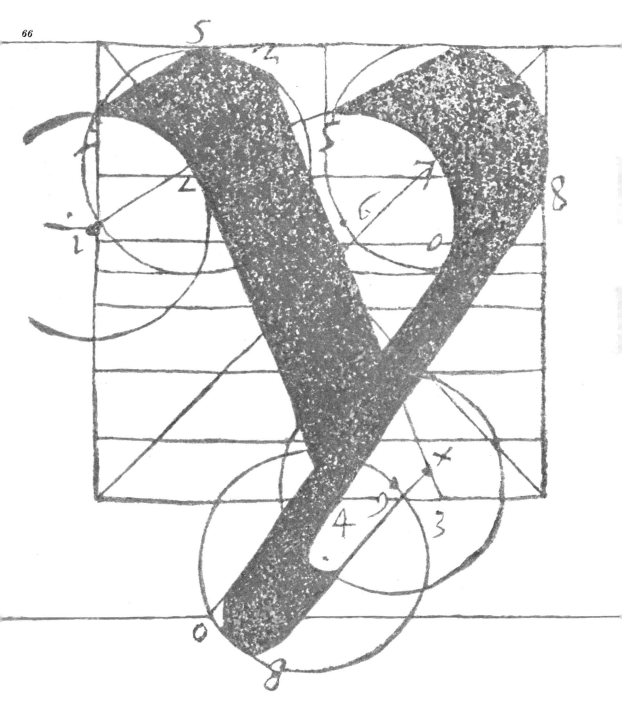

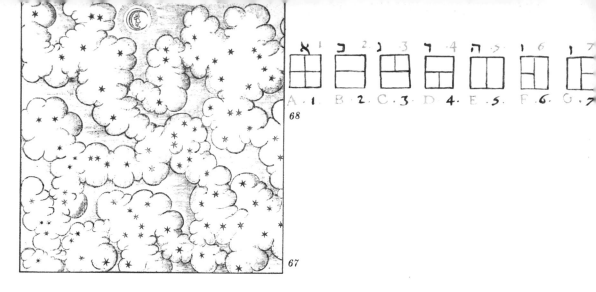

68

67

decorating of manuscripts with designs around the borders and with intricately worked, brightly colored initial letters.

By the thirteenth century Europe was emerging from its long intellectual slumber and a new dawn of learning was rising in the West. From the thirteenth to the fifteenth century more than 50 of Europe's great universities had their birth. To meet the scholarly demand for books, the universities set up their own ateliers of manuscript copyists. About the same time a hunger for literature developed among the nobility, from whom it spread to the rising bourgeoisie. As paper was not yet generally in use, a fine grade of parchment called vellum was the principal material upon which writing was inscribed. So intense was the yearning for books among the nobles that many kept their own house calligraphers, while others contracted for extremely expensive copies from the private ateliers that were now coming into existence to meet the demands of an ever-widening audience of readers. Certainly the best-made books of the period were wonders of beauty. Their bindings of leather or silver were sometimes set with precious stones, and the pages themselves were adorned with the highest expression of the illuminator's and copyist's art.

But these were for the nobility, and a market was fast developing for popular literature in the vernacular tongues. An oral literary tradition already existed through the minstrel's art, but now the middle classes were demanding books of their own, and for them cheaper copies, not so well made, began to be published. These were produced in considerable numbers and sold over the counter in much the same way that books are sold today. For example, over 2,000 hand-produced copies of the collected works of Aristotle, dating from the thirteenth and fourteenth centuries, still exist today. Since books are highly perishable, it is reasonable to assume that at least 50 times that number were originally produced. So popular had reading become that it was not unusual for a bookseller to order hundreds of copies of a new work whose contents he had never seen. He knew that any book could be sold.

But what of the authors? The primitive copyright laws of the Romans had long since lapsed, and anyone was at liberty to issue a new work without so much as contributing a penny to the support of the writer. To remedy this a system of patronage grew up. An author with a manuscript to sell—even one so famous as Boccaccio in the fourteenth century—would take it to a rich nobleman, offer him a flowery dedication, and if all went well, would be given a sum by the patron, who would then have the book luxuriously copied for his private collection. From that point on the matter was in the hands of the booksellers. An author known to be the protégé of a particularly celebrated duke or prince would see his work recopied in relatively cheap editions for sale to the bourgeoisie. But the writer would gain nothing from the "reprints" save the enhancement of his reputation.

By the middle of the fifteenth century the demand for books was so great that the need for a method of producing them cheaply had become imperative. Paper, by now in widespread use, was a partial answer (it is estimated that had the Gutenberg Bible been printed on vellum, about 170 skins would have been needed to produce a

67-68   Throughout the history of human communications, emphasis has been placed on an effort to convey meaning clearly from one person to another. But in certain cases, just the opposite has been true as men, whether for reasons of security in time of war, or through a fascination for the mystic and secretive, have worked out baffling codes and secret ways of writing. In this early 17th century code (67) the position of each star corresponds to a letter of the alphabte. A chart of the specially—arranged alphabet can be placed behind the star card in such a way that it is possible to decipher the message letter by letter. Cabalistic signs (68) are used by certain groups of people interested in the occult.

single copy). But the major breakthrough, of course, was the art of printing itself—first with blocks and then with movable type. Printing was originally developed by the Chinese, but their methods never reached the West. In Europe, however, beginning shortly after 1400, progress in the same direction began to be made. At first pictures and short captions were cut into blocks of wood and imprinted on paper. Then toward the middle of the century Johann Gensfleisch, known as Gutenberg, took the next, and decisive step with his invention of movable type. In 1456, in his native city of Mainz, Gutenberg issued the first book printed from movable type in the West—the Gutenberg (or Mazarin) Bible. Through the invention of movable type, exact reproductions of books became a possibility—each copy identical with the others, even down to the errors. In addition, Gutenberg developed molds, or matrices, from which individual letters could be cast, thus eliminating the laborious process of hand-cutting each character—an early application of the "theory of interchangeable parts," with all that that implies in terms of mass production. He also invented an ink which would adhere to metal type.

The Church and universities at first regarded the printed word with suspicion as somehow suspect because lacking the authority of the visible person, but booksellers, with their eye for commerce, saw in it something of much greater import, a method of quantity publication of new work as well as old, to be sold to the literate bourgeoisie at prices within their means. By 1480, only a few years after the date of the Gutenberg Bible, printing had spread to France,

the Netherlands, Spain, England, and most prominently of all to Italy, birthplace of the Renaissance, which at the time furnished almost half the total European production of books. By the sixteenth century, printing had taken on many of the characteristics of a modern business. Type was standardized, technical specialities were developed, and the publishing houses themselves, requiring large amounts of capital, sometimes employed as many as a hundred compositors, proofreaders, pressmen, illuminators, and binders. Fast as it had developed, printing was scarcely able to keep pace with the ever-rising demand for books, and great competition arose among the presses in the various European countries to provide their customers with a sufficient number of volumes, particularly in the native or national tongues.

From Gutenberg's time through the eighteenth century new printing techniques and new type designs also proliferated—but this process was very slow, thanks to the innate conservatism of the profession. The first printing was done in gothic type, but this was soon replaced through most of western Europe by roman and italic types, popularized by the great Venetian printer Aldus Manutius at the end of the fifteenth century. (Aldus also originated the concept of "pocket editions"—a series of scholarly books that were both compact and cheap. He printed as many as 1,000 copies of each edition, an immense number for that day.)

In 1725, a Scottish printer, William Ged, invented a process which later became known as "stereotypy": making a cast or mold of a metal plate from which a fresh plate could be produced whenever necessary, so that type

69

need not be reset for future reprints. A quarter century later another Briton, John Baskerville, developed a fine-quality paper which he named vellum, after the parchment. Here was clearly a case of necessity being the mother of invention, for Baskerville had also designed a new type face of a remarkably modern style, the use of which required paper of a finer quality than was available at the time. Baskerville is still one of the most popular type faces in the Western world.

Along with the rising demand for books came an almost insatiable appetite for illustrated editions, which some publishers sought to satisfy by commissioning great artists of the period, such as Albrecht Dürer, to do woodcuts. But others sought easier and cheaper methods. The 1,809 illustrations in Hartmann Schedel's *liber Chronicarum*, published in 1493, were made from only 645 woodblocks. The same picture of a city would appear several times, captioned "Rome," "Jerusalem," or "Paris" as the context demanded.

Something resembling the modern publishing industry was taking form. In the beginning the printer and publisher were one and the same. Slowly a differentiation developed between the two. The publisher provided the capital while the printer became a specialized craftsman who carried out the publisher's orders.

One beneficiary of the increasing rationalization of the publishing industry was the author. In 1709 Britain passed the first modern copyright law. It recognized that a manuscript was a valuable commodity to which the author had ultimate rights; only he could dispose of it on the open market to his best advantage. The law also protected publishers, who could now buy a manuscript reasonably secure in the knowledge that it would be safe from pirating. Other countries followed suit; in 1886 the International Copyright Convention was signed, establishing the principle of international reciprocity of rights. It has been supplemented by the Universal Copyright Convention of 1955, which protects authors and publishers throughout most of the non-Communist world.

The Industrial Revolution of the nineteenth century brought vast changes to the publishing industry. England, the fount of many of the era's great advances, was the first to benefit. In 1662 London had but 60 publishers: 200 years later it had almost 700. Germany and the United States also greatly increased their output of books. The rise of mass education had made it possible for the first time to sell books in large quantities to all classes of people. The potential market was almost inexhaustible, but to reach it many advances were needed. Cheaper paper made from wood pulp was developed, and the continuous paper-manufacturing process was first used in England in 1803. Hand setting was replaced by machine-set type: the first linotype machine was patented by the American Ottmar Mergenthaler in 1885 and the monotype machine by another American, Tolbert Lanston, in 1887. Cheaper paper, automatic typesetting, steam-operated and rotary presses, lithography were all inventions of the Industrial Revolution, and each contributed to the mass production of books, bringing literature, science, and philosophy into all but the meanest of western European and American homes.

69-70 *Illustrations from Athanasius Kircher's early 17th century work, "Musurgia Universalis." Music played inside a mansion (69) is picked up by a "loudspeaker" and broadcast to listeners outside the house. This primitive ancestor of the phonograph, and the electronic high fidelity and public address systems of today, depended upon a simple principle of physics—that sound can be transmitted for considerable distances by concentrating the waves and forcing them to travel in one direction. Examples are the speaking tube, megaphone, and trumpet (which also modulates the waves). 70 Military trumpets of Alexander the Great, as imagined by Kircher. The trumpet is one of the earliest devices used in military communications.*

70

Another development of the period was the public library. Libraries had existed for hundreds of years, but access to them had generally been limited. A so-called public library of the eighteenth century issued this regulation: "In order to check the previous excessive concourse in the best manner possible, anybody who wants to inspect a book has to apply to the librarian who then will show, and if need be, even allow him to read it." But the spread of education created a demand for libraries open to all. A public library was opened in Boston as early as 1653, although tax-supported libraries did not come into existence in the United States until 1833. Today every city of any size in the United States and Britain maintains a tax-supported library, and in larger cities many branches of a main library exist for the convenience of the borrower. In American rural areas, "bookmobiles" bring a varied fare to people who find it difficult to travel to urban centers. Concurrent with the rise of public libraries was the development of privately owned lending institutions, which charge the borrower a fee for the privilege of taking home the latest books.

Despite competition from radio, television, and the motion pictures, books are not likely to disappear from our lives in the foreseeable future. For, as the Russian author Maxim Gorki once said, expressing the sentiments of millions, "I love books. Each one is really a miracle. When I have a new volume in my hands, an object made in a printing shop by the hands of a heroic typographer, with the help of a machine invented by another hero, I feel that something living, speaking, marvelous has come into my life."

71   An elaborate "eavesdropping" system, supposed to have been developed by Denis, Tyrant of Syracuse, who ruled from 405 to 367 B.C., and imagined here by Athanasius Kircher in a strictly baroque setting. Again working on the principle of condensing or containing sound waves to make them carry over great distances, the palace of Denis was supposed to have been riddled with funnels, which picked up court gossip and transmitted it to "speakers" hidden behind busts. By stationing trusted men at these posts, Denis was able to keep abreast of what his courtiers were discussing, and thus inform himself of any brewing unrest or revolution. Rather similar, but decidedly harmless, speaking tubes were installed in 19th century homes or stores to facilitate the giving of orders.

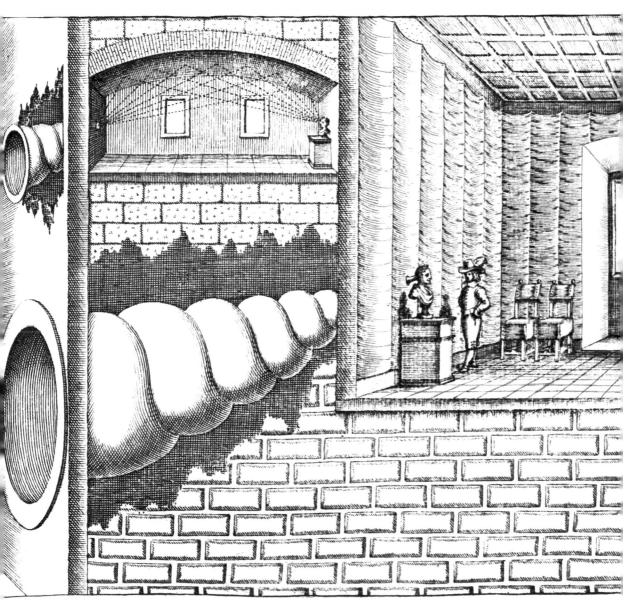

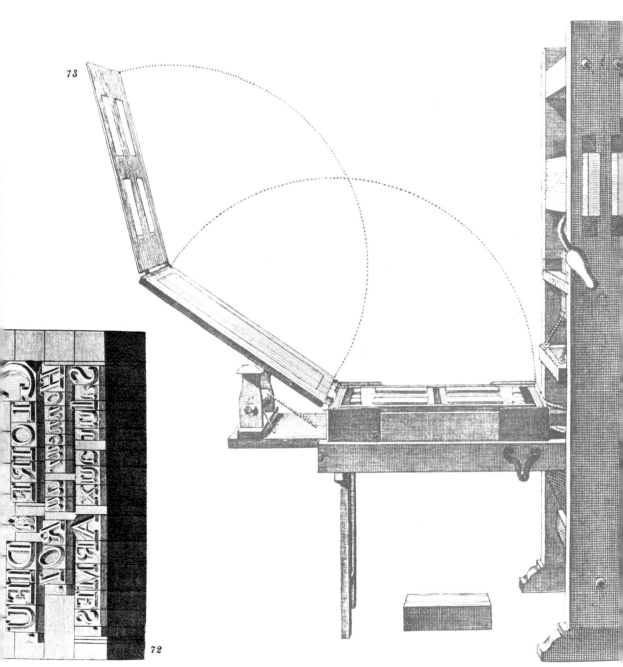

72-74 Illustrations from Diderot's great "Encyclopédie"
show aspects of 18th century printing, such as a form (72)
complete with type ready to be printed, an 18th century
printing press (73), and a method of placing composed
type in a galley (74).

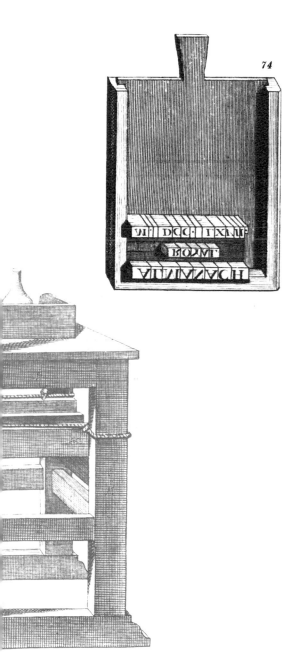

74

Today's press had its origins in the Roman *Acta diurna*, official announcements which were first posted for public reading in 131 B.C. Julius Caesar, in 59 B.C., also ordered publication of senate debates, but it was not long before this practice roused the ire of the ruling elite, and the *Acta senatus* fell under the deadening influence of official censorship, an early example of an evil which has plagued journalism from the beginning.

After the fall of Rome, the press, such as it was, suffered a complete demise. Its rebirth did not come about until the beginning of the modern era, and its impetus was not politics, but commerce. The earliest examples of journalism appeared during the first half of the sixteenth century. These were handwritten "newsletters," published at irregular intervals, which private commercial firms, such as the powerful Augsburg house of Fugger, circulated among their employees and certain favored customers. The commercial revolution was in full swing, and merchants were anxious for news of financial transactions and shipping. Government intervention in business made a knowledge of political happenings important to the merchant, and so the newsletters began to carry such items as supplements. In time these newsletters grew into veritable newspapers.

By the middle of the sixteenth century, printers began to see the profitable possibilities in publishing news for an unrestricted audience. The first such journals were in the form of pamphlets, known as "newsbooks," dating in Britain from September 9, 1513, when a pamphlet entitled "The trewe encountre of the battle of Flodden Field" was published. Such newsbooks were

not true newspapers, as they were devoted to only one subject per issue. Not until almost a century later did newspapers of general interest begin to appear with some regularity. The first was a German publication, *Avisa Relation oder Zeitung*, dating from 1609; this was followed by the *Nieuwe Tijdinghen* of Antwerp (1616) and the *Gazette de France* in Paris (1631).

An early peculiarity of the "weekly" press was that it did not appear weekly but spasmodically. Publication dates depended upon the arrival of the mails, which in that period were notoriously undependable. The English press, which relied in large measure on news from the continent, was for that reason even more at the mercy of the mails than papers across the Channel. But British editors more than made up for this by their almost uncanny instinct for featuring news that would appeal to their audience. Even the earliest "weeklies" were careful to give much space to the heroic actions of Englishmen abroad.

As newspapers grew to be an accepted part of life in western Europe, they gave rise to another form of journalism, the magazine. The first magazines were highly specialized, but in 1672 the French led the way toward a popular periodical with the *Mercure Galant*, which included a variety of features such as poetry, social news, and literary criticism. Soon a periodical was appearing in Leipzig whose stated purpose was to be "entertaining and serious, (featuring) rational and unsophisticated ideas on all kinds of agreeable and useful books and subjects"— goals which characterize many leading popular magazines today. As the mails became more reliable, publishers were able to regularize their

printing schedules, and finally the daily newspaper made its appearance with the publication of the *Daily Courant* of London in 1702. Other dailies soon began publication in Switzerland and France. The press was not yet truly independent, for everywhere censorship regulations were strict. But forces were at work that would soon challenge a government's right to inhibit the free flow of the news.

In 1644 John Milton's *Areopagitica* was published in Britain. It boldly attacked the practice of licensing (and thus controlling) printers. Although Milton wrote in terms of books, his essay was to have at least as great an effect on newspaper publishing. "As good almost kill a man as kill a good book," he wrote. "Who kills a man kills a reasonable creature; but he who destroys a book kills reason itself, the image of God." Ironically, it was a plagiarism of Milton's original text, half a century later, that brought the matter of control to public attention, and in 1695 Parliament finally discontinued the Licensing Act.

Actually it was not the newspapermen of the era, but pamphleteers and writers for the highly cultivated journals of opinion who first took advantage of the new freedom. In the early eighteenth century men like Addison and Steele, Daniel Defoe, and the incomparable Jonathan Swift sharpened their wits on the abuses and follies of government. Soon the newspapers were emboldened to follow the example set by their more courageous journalistic brethren, and in 1712 the British government struck back by establishing a stamp tax on all newspapers, which kept their prices artificially high, thus restricting circulation.

75-77 Printing in the 18th century, from the "Encyclopédie." Typesetters work in the composing room (75) while other printers run the presses (77).
76 Théophraste Renaudot (1568-1653) founded the news pamphlet "Gazette de France" in 1631 under the sponsorship of Richelieu. A century earlier, the big trading companies had begun to circulate hand-written newsletters, probably the earliest form of newspaper. From these developed the news pamphlet, the news sheet, and finally, during the 17th century, the newspaper and the periodical. Daily newspapers began to replace the bi- or tri-weekly papers early in the 18th century. At the same time the evening paper made its appearance and weekly, monthly, and quarterly periodicals began to become popular.

77

Another, even more pernicious method used by the British to limit freedom of the press was the application of libel laws so strict that any attack on a parliamentarian, whether justified or not, could bring conviction. The publication of parliamentary debates had to be accomplished through subterfuge, and journals took to describing events in Commons or Lords as having happened in mythical places—such as Lilliput. This issue and its companion abuse—the general warrant under which all persons, however vaguely associated with a "libel," could be charged with an offense—came to a head in the case of John Wilkes. An essayist and politician, Wilkes had long been a critic of both king and ministry. In 1763, in his publication *The North Briton*, he made a direct attack upon King George III. Under a general warrant Wilkes and 48 others were arrested. But the trial judge released Wilkes and declared the general warrant illegal, thus destroying the basis of the practice in law. Henceforth the government could issue warrants only against those charged with instituting and printing the libel. As for Wilkes, he was again charged with libel and convicted, but the case aroused such a storm that it led to the passage of the Libel Act of 1792, which empowered juries, instead of judges alone, to determine whether a libel had been committed. Even so, it was not until 1868 that British law admitted truth as a defense against a libel action.

If reform moved rather slowly in the mother country, it advanced with amazing speed in the American colonies. The colonists, remote from the political brawls of Parliament and ever conscious of their rights as "free-born Englishmen," were quick to establish newspapers in the New World. The first was Boston's *Publick Occurrences*, which appeared in 1690, only to be suppressed after one issue by the royal governor. But where the first had failed many others succeeded, and though they often faced persecution by the authorities colonial newspapers flourished and expanded. The decisive moment for American journalism came in 1734, when a New York editor, John Peter Zenger, was arrested on charges of libeling the colony's governor. The trial, at which Zenger was acquitted established that, in America at least, no man could be convicted of libel for telling the truth. The Zenger episode marked the real beginnings of a free press in the British colonies—a concept that became one of the guiding principles of American democracy, as may be seen in the First Amendment to the Federal Constitution, which specifically bars Congress from enacting any law "abridging the freedom of speech, or of the press."

As the principles of liberty were inching ahead in Britain and leaping forward in America, they were merely limping about in circles in France. Until the French Revolution, journalism was subject to the arbitrary and capricious measures of the monarchy. The revolutionary government at first sought to guarantee the rights of the press, and in the halcyon days of the new freedom, between 1789 and 1793, Paris alone blossomed forth with more than 1,000 different newspapers. Napoleon Bonaparte changed all that. "If I give the press free rein," he said in 1799, "I shall not stay three months in power." Parisian newspapers were eventually reduced to four, none of them more than propaganda organs for the emperor.

78-79   In spite of the quick advances
in printing, the art of writing
was still assiduously studied in
the 18th century, as is attested by
this plate (79) from Saint-Omer's
"Graphométrie" of 1790. The position
of the writer, his manner of holding
the pen (always a quill pen— see
also 78), the shapes of the pen nibs
themselves, as well as the actual
pursuit of the study of writing
and the form of the letters, all come
into consideration in this very
thorough manual. Our contemporary
handwriting has been neglected and
deformed by the dominance of the typewriter. But one aspect of handwriting—
graphology, or the reading of character
from handwriting—is still held in
high esteem by many people today.

79

The rise of journalism to its present eminence did not depend on liberty alone, but also on technical innovations, and the nineteenth century gave birth to those inventions which form the basis of newspaper publishing today. In 1814 *The Times* of London placed in operation the first cylindrical steam-powered press, which produced 1,100 news sheets an hour. By the 1850's the cost of paper had been greatly reduced by the invention of a practical method for making newsprint from wood pulp. This, combined with the invention of the rotary press and the linotype and monotype machines, made the publication of truly mass-based newspapers a possibility that enterprising publishers were quick to seize upon. The linotype, mentioned in Chapter III, replaced the laborious hand setting of type. The rotary press, designed by the American Richard March Hoe in 1846-47, immensely increased the speed of printing: by 1866 it was capable of producing 10,500 copies of *The Times* per hour.

Two other inventions of the period had incalculable effects on both the popular and "quality" press. One was the telegraph, which flashed news all over the world in a matter of hours instead of days or weeks; and the other was photography. The photographic process owes much of its early success to two nineteenth century Frenchmen, Nicéphore Niepce and Jacques Daguerre. In 1822 Niepce succeeded in making the first photograph by exposing a surface sensitive to light within a camera. In 1829 Niepce began his association with Daguerre, and the two men worked together on improving Niepce's invention. In 1837 Daguerre discovered that images could be developed on a metal plate coated with a thin layer of silver iodide—

81 *The first postage stamp, 1840, showing the head of young Queen Victoria of England. Before the introduction of prepaid postage stamps, the sending of letters was a hazardous matter. In backwoods America they were often entrusted to peddlers, who would leave them at the local inn or general store. Naturally, many were lost.*
80-82 *Before the invention of the typewriter, letters and almost all other documents were written by hand. The teaching of calligraphy was thus far more important than it is today. An early 17th century writing manual (80), by the professor of calligraphy to Louis XIII of France, shows the italic script. An 18th century French manual by Crépy Fils (82) illustrates the writing of capital letters.*

81

82

83

the daguerreotype. Later came the use of paper instead of metal, and in 1841 the negative-positive or calotype process was patented. Finally, in 1884, the American George Eastman introduced roll film, which opened the era of home photography. But newspapers did not wait until photography was perfected before adapting it to journalism. Within two years of Daguerre's invention, after processes had been developed for adapting the photograph to newspaper use, three major illustrated journals were on sale in Europe: *The Illustrated London News*, *Illustration* in France, and *Illustrierte Zeitung* in Leipzig. Not for many years, however, was the typical woodcut and steel engraving of the popular magazine entirely replaced by photography.

Another advance of the period was the international news agency, which makes available to its subscribers the services of hundreds of reporters stationed around the globe. The first was the French Agence Havas, founded by Charles Havas in 1835. This was followed by the Wolff Agency of Berlin in the later 1830's, Reuter's of Britain in 1851, and the Associated Press of the United States in the 1890's.

All this progress would have been relatively meaningless without a literate audience ready to take up the newspaper-reading habit. The compulsory-education laws of the nineteenth century provided such an audience, and it remained only for farsighted publishers to tap the curiosity of the masses. France early took the leadership in this field when Emile de Girardin launched *La Presse* in 1836. By offering his newspaper at half the price charged by others, de Girardin was able to build its circulation from 10,000 to 63,000 within ten years. After the

Revolution of 1848, which re-established freedom of the press in France, others followed de Girardin's example: in 1854, *Le Figaro*, aimed at a middle class audience, appeared, and it was followed in 1863 by *Le Petit Journal*, which sought a working-class readership.

In Britain, meanwhile, one of the most remarkable journalistic institutions in history, *The Times* of London, was growing to its position of pre-eminence in the world of newspapers. First published in 1785 (under the title *The Daily Universal Register*, which was changed to *The Times* in 1788), it gave no hint of its future role. Its publisher, John Walter, contented himself with commercial news and scandal. But the search for scandal led him to build the most efficient reporting staff then in existence. His son, John Walter II, who took over management of the paper at the start of the nineteenth century, had a very different approach. With the famed editor, Thomas Barnes, he built *The Times* into an organ admirably suited to the tastes and needs of Britain's rising middle class. Barnes was probably the first journalist to recognize the power of public opinion, when properly channeled through a newspaper, and he made *The Times* into a strong arm of the middle class in its epic battle for political reform. So well did he achieve this goal that by the time he was succeeded by the equally illustrious John T. Delane in 1841, *The Times* no longer had to reckon with governmental disapproval—it was the government that feared *The Times*. Indeed, *The Times* soon became the semi-official spokesman for the government itself, irrespective of which party was in power. Under Delane the paper improved upon its already

83-84 *French physicist Nicéphore Niepce, 1765-1833 (83) and Parisian inventor Jacques Daguerre, 1789-1851 (84) worked independently on photography in the early 19th century. By 1824 Niepce had taken his first photograph, "Table Laid for a Meal," exposed for 14 hours. After 1829, Daguerre and Niepce collaborated, publishing a treatise on their mutual discovery. Niepce did not live to see his invention perfected, but Daguerre continued to work, making mostly landscape and still life photographs, for his system still required a half hour of exposure. By 1851 exposure time had been cut to a few seconds, and the new process of using plate glass negatives made it possible to produce an unlimited number of prints on paper.*

84

enviable position, and it was said that there was no state secret safe from its prying reporters.

The great contribution of *The Times* of London was the firm establishment in British journalism of the concept that a newspaper was an entirely independent body, responsible not to the government but to public opinion. Also to *The Times* goes the credit for employing the first war correspondent, William Howard Russell, whose reports on the management of the Crimean War helped bring down the cabinet in 1855.

But *The Times* was not a popular journal in the sense of *Le Petit Journal*, and the stamp duty on newspapers, which remained in force until 1855, prevented the early growth of the "penny press" in Britain. It was the United States that took over the leadership in this field from France, mostly through the pioneering of the James Gordon Bennetts, father and son. The senior Bennett came to the United States from Scotland in 1819, and in 1835 he launched the *New York Herald* at a penny a copy. Recognizing that spectacular and sensational items were indispensable in popular journalism, he spared no expense in gathering news of this type. His son, who took over the paper in 1867, went one step further. He conceived the notion that a newspaper should not only report the news but make it. In 1869 he sent Henry Stanley off to the jungles of Africa in the famous search for the missionary, Dr. David Livingstone. The successful hunt cost $24,000—a large sum in those days—but the publicity was worth much more, and Bennett had the scoop of the age.

Joseph Pulitzer and William Randolph Hearst followed in the trail blazed by the two Bennetts. Pulitzer's New York *World*, which he bought in 1883, and Hearst's *Journal*, purchased in 1885, engaged in a bitter struggle for the allegiance of thousands of the city's underprivileged. Both papers specialized in crusades for municipal reform and labor's rights, and circulation was sought through bright, lively writing, a healthy smattering of scandal, and the first color comic strips. In these categories Hearst far outstripped his rival, but Pulitzer eventually built his *World* into a newspaper that was almost everything a popular journal should be—sprightly, attractive, crusading, and intelligently liberal.

By the turn of the century popular journalism had come of age, and there has been little essential change since then. But what of the future? In both America and Britain, circulation is growing, but the actual number of newspapers available is steadily shrinking. High costs have forced hundreds of papers to cease publication in the last three decades. The single-paper town is now almost the rule, and without competition it is doubtful whether the press can meet its obligations to its readers. The cold war, moreover, has added to the press's burdens, for the editor is sometimes faced with the delicate problem of balancing his obligation to inform the public against government's need to suppress some information in the interest of national security. But a free press is the foundation of our liberties, and hence of our national security itself; for as Thomas Jefferson said, "Were it left to me to decide whether we should have a government without newspapers or newspapers without government I should not hesitate a moment to prefer the latter."

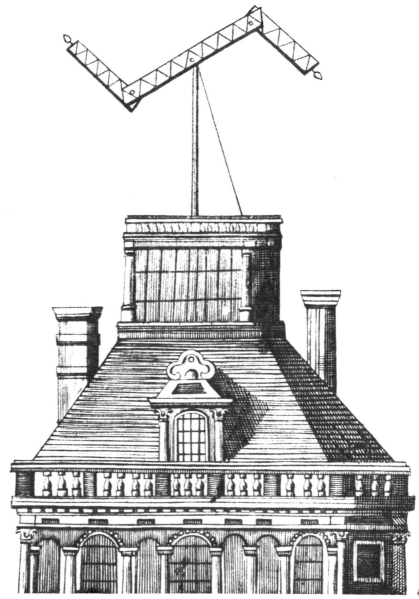

85 *Alphabet of signals devised for the optical telegraph*
(86) invented by Frenchman Claude Chappe (87) during
the French revolution. In 1794 a chain of these telegraphs,
set up on hill tops, was built to connect Paris with
Lille, and quickly relayed word of a French victory.

The newspaper delivered to one's door is a blend of one of the older methods of communications with many newer forms dating from the mid-nineteenth century right up to the present decade. Local news is probably telephoned into the city room; national and foreign items are received via the telegraph or teletype. The paper itself may be set in type through a new automated process known as teletypesetting. Pictures taken hundreds of miles away are received through the medium of wirephoto or radiophoto. On the entertainment pages of the paper appear reports on television, radio, and the movies. All these items have two things in common: they are means of communicating over distances (the Greek prefix "tele" means "in the distance") and in one way or another all are dependent on electricity.

Man did not have to wait for the age of electricity to communicate through space. There were many primitive methods, such as Indian smoke signals, African drum beats, and light beacons. Although Greeks, Romans, Carthaginians, Gauls, and many others had methods of relaying news, these were unreliable at best, for there were so many human intermediaries between the source and the recipient that the message was most likely to be garbled in transit. At the very threshhold of the electric era, in 1794, a French engineer, Claude Chappe, invented an optical telegraph that was widely used. Its stations were equipped with a signalling system consisting of three movable pieces of wood operated by strings and pulleys. These were set atop high buildings or mountains at close intervals and operators would signal from one station to the next. By 1844, this system

87

88

88-90 *Since earliest times the need,
both military and civilian, for sending
messages to distant points with rapidity
had been great but the means inadequate.
Until the invention of the electric
telegraph, carrier pigeons, relay
messengers on foot or on horseback,
signal fires, and other devices had been
used. A descendant of the signal fire
is the French military "blinker" apparatus
of 1898 (88) pictured here. It was
the electric telegraph, worked out in its
most practical form by the American
Samuel F. B. Morse (89) in 1837, which
finally solved the problem. The ancestors
of the telegraph were legion, and at least
three other systems were launched in 1837
alone. The "sender" of a Breguet telegraph
system (90) of 1849 is shown below.*

89

90

92

91

93

91   Portrait of Alexander Graham
Bell (1847-1922), Scottish-born
inventor of the telephone,
which he patented in 1876.
92   Early 20th century
pamphlet of instructions for setting
up rural telephone systems in the
United States. The telephone
became a potent social
instrument for bringing farmers
into contact with one another
and the outside world.
93   A telephone central exchange
in Nuremberg, Germany, in 1905.
94   An elaborate oaken wall
telephone of 1903, made in the
United States for use in phone
booths and businesses.

94

95
96

97

95 Thomas Alva Edison (1847-1931),
best known for his invention of the
incandescent electric lamp in 1879,
also invented the phonograph in 1877, and
the "kinetoscope," a motion picture system.
96 Guglielmo Marconi (1874-1937),
inventor and electrician, pioneered
wireless communication at the turn of
the last century. In 1901 he transmitted
wireless signals from England to
Newfoundland, and within a few years
ships at sea were using his system to
keep in contact with the shore.
97 This wireless telegraph atop
the Eiffel Tower was tested in 1898.
98 By the beginning of the 20th century
the Victor phonograph, identified by its
famous dog and the slogan "His master's
voice," was known around the world.

98

99 Georges Méliès (1861-1938) was
a great pioneer of the cinema in France.
In his short but active career (1895-1914)
Méliès made some four thousand reels of
film and introduced many new techniques.
He was a magician at heart, delighting
in trick photography, fantastic sets,
outlandish plots. His motion pictures
showed a unique combination of imaginative
and scientific inventiveness. The 1906
film "The Wicked Fairy" (99) was
Méliès at his best—full of haunted
castles and witches in pointed hats.
100 Magic lantern slide, late 18th
century. Made in two parts, the slide
was a primitive kind of motion picture—
when one part of the slide was pushed
over the other, the long-billed demon
seemed to throw his victim into the
jaws of the hungry dragon.

100

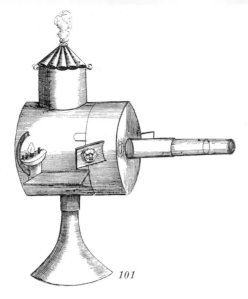

101

connected 29 French cities through 500 stations covering more than 3,000 miles. Weather permitting, a message could be sent, for instance, over the more than 500 miles between Paris and Toulon in only 20 minutes.

By this time man had gained some understanding of the properties of electricity, and early efforts were being made to put it to use in the service of humanity, particularly in the field of communications. As early as 1812 an electric telegraph, using many wires, had been put into operation. In 1837 at least three telegraph systems were launched, including Cooke and Wheatstone's in England. But the most practical proved to be that of the American Samuel F. B. Morse, whose invention of a code of dots and dashes, sent by making and breaking the current in the circuit in a series of audible clicks, made it possible to transmit messages over great distances in a matter of minutes. A few years after Morse's first successful demonstration, his telegraph lines linked most of the major American cities. Twenty-one years after the introduction of the telegraph, a cable was laid under the Atlantic to link the Old World with the New, and though salt water corrosion of the cable soon caused communications to break down, the point had been proved and in 1866 a new and completely successful attempt was made. Europe and America have been telegraphically linked ever since. By the 1870's, almost one and a quarter million miles of wire and cable linked distant parts of the world, and in 1903 President Theodore Roosevelt participated in the first round-the-world telegraph experiment; his message was relayed in only nine minutes.

Meanwhile, as telegraph lines were encircling the earth, a new invention was capturing the imagination of Western man. For centuries the idea of speaking directly to people who were at a distance had tantalized researchers and scientists. Here was the germ of the telephone, a name employed as early as 1796 to describe the instrument we now call a megaphone. A century earlier, in 1667, Robert Hooke had invented a mechanical telephone, much like a child's homemade phone of today in which a string, connecting two cans, transmits sound waves from one to the other. Yet such devices were little more than toys, and it remained for the Scottish-born American, Alexander Graham Bell, to synthesize the work of past experimenters and add some concepts of his own in order to develop the first practical telephone. He had said: "If I could make a current of electricity vary in intensity precisely as the air varies in density during the production of sound, I should be able to transmit speech telegraphically."

Building upon this principle, Bell experimented with various devices for transmitting and receiving. On June 3, 1875, he succeeded in transmitting speech electrically, and on March 10, 1876, the first complete sentence—the famous "Mr. Watson, come here, I want you" —was carried over electric wire. But many improvements would have to be made before the telephone became a practical device. Bell's first telephone delivered such feeble electrical currents as to be almost useless. But improvements were made, thanks to men like Thomas Edison, and by 1915 transcontinental service had been inaugurated in North America.

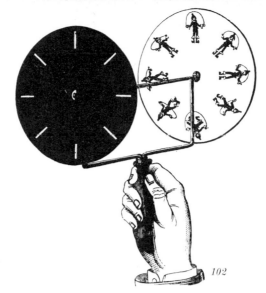

101 Magic lantern of the 17th century. In this early form of slide projector the light from the flame, reflected by a mirror, projects the image on the glass plate onto a screen. During the 17th century the magic lantern was enthusiastically adopted in fashionable salons as well as at popular fairs.
102 The "phenakistiscope," an ancestor of the cinema, which gave the illusion of movement through persistent optical sensations.
103-114 (Next page.) In the "phenakistiscope," a series of drawings, as seen on these cards, was viewed through the slits in another card while both were spinning, giving a vivid illusion of motion.

Today there are more than 130 million telephones in use throughout the world; over 70 million of these are in the United States alone, and they are served by 35 million miles of wire on 260,000 miles of route. Transatlantic telephone service has existed since 1927, and conversations between America and Europe are now a commonplace occurrence in the affairs of any large business organization.

Telegraph and telephone have two major things in common: both employ wires and both are essentially a means of person-to-person communication. At the close of the nineteenth century, the newspaper, the magazine, and the book were still the chief media of mass communications. But with the introduction of wireless telegraphy, which led directly to the medium we know as radio, the monopoly of the printed word was about to be broken. The advent of the telegraph speeded research. But it was not until 1869 that the Scottish physicist James Clerk Maxwell provided a theoretical base for experiments in transmitting sound through space without wires. Maxwell postulated the idea that electromagnetic waves move through space at the speed of light. In 1887, using Maxwell's theory as the basis of his own experiments, a German scientist, Heinrich Hertz, created electromagnetic waves by means of a spark discharge, detected them on a primitive receiving antenna, and measured their velocity—which proved to be, as Maxwell had thought, the speed of light. These "Hertzian waves" formed the basis of radio.

The practical development of wireless telegraphy soon followed, due mostly to an Italian, Guglielmo Marconi. While still in his teens,

Marconi chanced upon an article in an electrical journal which told of Hertz's experiments and his success in creating and transmitting electromagnetic waves over very short distances. His imagination fired, Marconi decided to develop a system of wireless telegraphy. Happily, he came from a wealthy family and thus had the leisure to pursue his interest. As much a synthesizer of the work of others as an inventor, Marconi went at his task with a will, confident that he would ultimately succeed and fearing only that others might fit together the pieces of the electrical puzzle before he could do so. Success came to Marconi much earlier than perhaps even he believed possible. Improving upon the methods of Hertz, by 1896 he was able to transmit signals over a nine-mile distance. All that remained was to develop improvements on existing methods. By 1899 Marconi was sending messages across the English Channel, and in 1901 he succeeded in establishing a wireless link between North America and Europe.

As the invention of the telegraph had led to speculations on the possibility of transmitting speech over wires, so the invention of the wireless fathered the concept later on of transmitting speech through the air. The idea originally had nothing to do with a medium of mass communications, but rather it was seen as a method of person-to-person, ship-to-ship, and ship-to-shore contact. An American, Reginald Aubrey Fessenden, was perhaps the first to explore these possibilities thoroughly. Theorizing that a continuous radio wave was like a sustained musical note which could be modulated to the shape of articulate speech, he achieved in 1900 the feat of broadcasting speech over a distance of one

103

106

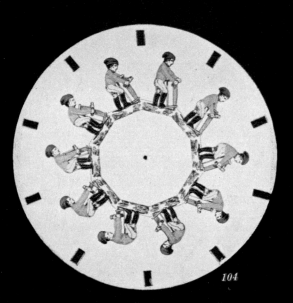

104

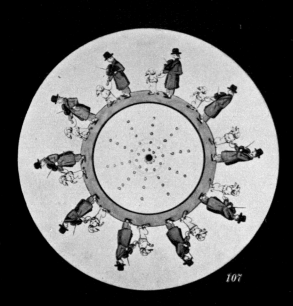

107

105

108

109

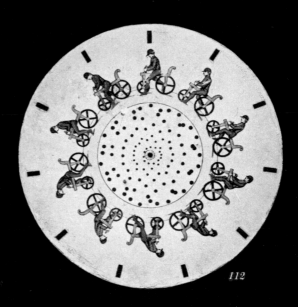

112

110

113

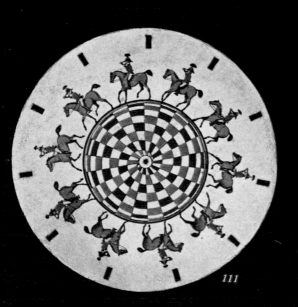

111

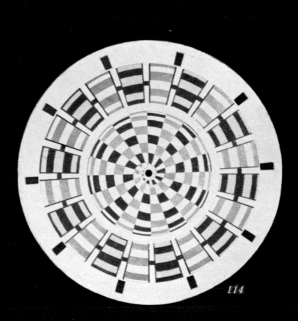

114

115

mile. By 1903 he was able to increase the range to 25 miles, then three years later held a wireless conversation with an associate 200 miles away. This was, essentially, radio; but the primitive means employed to transmit and detect the waves were so uncertain that it was still little more than a fascinating gadget. It would take the new science of electronics to fashion radio into the first medium of instant mass communications.

In 1897, the English physicist Sir Joseph John Thomson verified the existence of the electron as the smallest particle of the atom's electrical structure. If the electron could be harnessed, its power might be used to modulate, amplify, and detect the electromagnetic waves. In 1904, Sir John Ambrose Fleming devised the electronic two-element vacuum tube for just such purposes. Two years later an American, Lee De Forest, improved upon this with his three-element tube, called the audion, which became the basis of modern radio, television, radar, and a host of other means of electronic communication. But De Forest was not only an inventor, he was also something of a showman, and he was among the first to recognize the possibilities of radio for entertainment. In 1910 he succeeded in transmitting a broadcast from the Metropolitan Opera House, and "ham" (or amateur) wireless operators as well as ships off New York picked up the strains of Caruso's voice.

America's entry into World War I temporarily closed down the little boom in radio ham operations, but the widespread use to which wireless was put during the war as a means of military communication added luster to its

image in the popular mind. At this time most people still thought of it as a device for conversation, like the telephone, but not so a young man named David Sarnoff. While working for the American Marconi Company in 1916, Sarnoff wrote this report to his superiors: "I have in mind a plan of development which would make radio a household utility. The idea is to bring music into the home by wireless. The receiver can be designed in the form of a simple 'radio music box,' and arranged for several different wave lengths which should be changeable with the throwing of a single switch or the pressing of a single button. The same principle can be extended to numerous other fields, as for example, receiving lectures at home which would be perfectly audible. Also, events of national importance can be simultaneously announced and received. Baseball scores can be transmitted in the air. This proposition would be especially interesting to farmers and others living in outlying districts." Sarnoff became commercial manager of the Radio Corporation of America when it was founded in 1920, and his vision of radio as a means of entertainment and education was soon realized in the postwar boom of the 1920's.

While radio was making a reality of the instantaneous transmission of the voice and music through space, another kind of "music box," the phonograph, was also entering the home. Thomas A. Edison's first crude sound-recording device was demonstrated in 1877. About 10 years later Emile Berliner replaced the Edison cylinder with a flat disk, or record, made of glass with a thin layer of varnish into which the grooves were engraved. Shortly after

115-116 *Japanese calligraphy, or the art of writing, introduced originally from China, was brought to a high point of perfection in the island kingdom. Even today, fine calligraphy is much admired and assiduously practised in Japan. The prints on these pages illustrate a late 18th century writing lesson (116) and the preparation of written prayers (115) to be fastened on temple doors.*

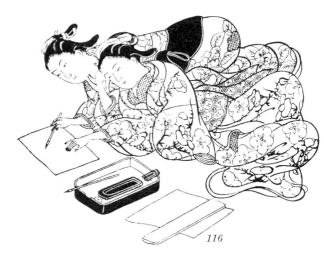

116

1900, records began to be made of a hardened plastic material. The modern phonograph was born when, again, electronics was called upon to amplify the hitherto rather faint and scratchy sound. Electronic phonographs were first marketed in 1927. In 1948 came the "long-playing" (33 1/3 r.p.m.) record which led to the present enormous proliferation of recorded sound.

About the same time as radio and the phonograph, another form of mass communications was also taking shape, the cinema. Motion pictures are in fact not that at all; they are a series of still pictures projected in a sequence so rapid as to give the illusion of motion. As an idea it is an old one indeed, and serial drawings were long attached to wheel-like devices which were spun so that the viewer could see men or horses "in action." But it was not until the 1870's that serial photographs could be taken at a high enough speed to give the effect of movement. In the 1890's, Thomas Edison developed his Kinetograph, a motion-picture camera using celluloid film, and the Kinetoscope, a mechanism for peep-show viewing, which was an immediate commercial success and whetted the public's appetite for "movies."

In 1895 the Lumière brothers of France developed the Cinematograph, the first practical method for projecting motion pictures on screens, and their technical discovery was complemented by the work of another Frenchman, Georges Méliès, whose creative imagination brought not only many technical innovations to film-making but also a rich vein of magic and fantasy. Between 1895 and 1914 Méliès produced more than 4,000 reels of film. The rest is well known. From these early inventions others followed, the process of motion picture production was refined, theaters were built all over the world, sound was added to sight, then color processes were developed for a burgeoning industry that has been entertaining, informing, educating, infuriating, and sometimes misleading hundreds of millions of people for more than half a century.

In much the same manner that wire communications gave rise to wireless, radio gave rise, if not to television itself, at least to an interest in developing it. For conceptually, and to a very limited degree in practice, by the time wireless was in use television already existed. The first experiments date back to 1873, when it was discovered that the element selenium, when exposed to different degrees of light, exhibited a variation in its electrical conductivity. A number of television experiments were based upon this knowledge, but the reactions of selenium were too slow for practical applications. Still, early television devices did succeed in projecting diffuse images over short spaces through the use of selenium and a mechanical scanning disk. The latter, invented by Paul Nipkow of Germany in 1884, was a spirally perforated disk which revolved in front of a light-sensitive picture, "cutting up" the image for broadcasting. The image was reproduced by means of a receiver with a luminous area, which was also scanned by a disk synchronized with that of the transmitter. The receiving disk "rearranged" the picture that the transmitting disk had "cut up."

Most early research in television took advantage of this mechanical device, and much progress was made, especially by John Baird

THE STAMP GALOP

Saxony. Tuscany.  United States.  Australia.  France.  Hamburgh. England.

India.  Naples. Germany. Prussia.  Germany. Papal States.  Lubeck.

Switzerland. Germany. Victoria. United States.  Italy. Russia. England.

French Repub. India. Naples.  Austria. Brunswick. Western Australia. Oldenburgh.

Spain. Prussia. Belgium. Greece. India. Hanover. Denmark.

Bavaria. Austria. Italy. England.  Switzerland. Prussia. Baden.

COMPOSED BY
ARTHUR O'LEARY.

ENT. STA. HALL.   PRICE 2/.

LONDON, EWER & C?
PARIS, G. FLAXLAND   LEIPZIG, C. F. LEEDE.

Lith. Anst. v. C. & Röder, Leipzig.

*117   The cover of a 19th century
popular dance, "The Stamp Galop"
illustrates two very different aspects of
human communication—music, and
the writing and sending of letters. Before
the middle of the 19th century, when
postage stamps began to come into general
use, letters were sent by messengers, by
postboys, or by regularly scheduled
stagecoaches. The postage was usually
paid by the person receiving the letter.
After 1840 postage stamps became popular
partly because they provided a source of
revenue for the many little states and
sovereign cities of 19th century Europe.*

in England and Barthélémy in France. But the mechanical approach was eventually to be discarded in favor of the more promising electronic method. In 1895 Sir William Crookes invented the cathode-ray tube. Its unusual properties were not explored until the early twentieth century, when Carl Ferdinand Braun of Germany saw in it a possibility for reproducing pictures in motion, if only the emission of electrons could be controlled. It was left to the Russo-American scientist Vladimir K. Zworykin to achieve this effect with an electronic scanning device or "eye" that could produce images of fine definition. In 1923 Zworykin invented the iconoscope, a cathode-ray tube that could be used for transmitting, and he followed this with the kinescope, a tube with a fluorescent screen for receiving. Television was now an all-electronic device, no longer dependent on moving parts.

The major developments were complete, and what remained to be done was to convince radio manufacturers and network executives that they should plow back some of their profits into the perfection of Zworykin's inventions. In the 1920's radio was in its heyday, and television seemed remote and slightly exotic. But Zworykin must have been something of a supersalesman, for he convinced the Radio Corporation of America to invest in his inventions, and the organization spent $50 million on research before producing the first commercial television receiver. Not until 1939 did R.C.A. consider television sufficiently developed to be marketable. On April 30, at the opening of the World's Fair in New York, it inaugurated what was to be a regular semi-weekly television service. After the United States' entry into World War II,

the government halted all civilian television production, although military research was to produce many advances in television that could be adapted to postwar use.

When the war ended, a market already existed for television, and the American public, with money to spend, eagerly awaited the advent of a new era in mass communications. Prewar television sets had large screens—but they were mirrors set on the top of an unwieldy box. The first postwar sets, having but 7 or ten-inch screens, were expensive, but nevertheless sold widely. Mass-production techniques and refinements on existing processes soon enlarged the screens and brought down the prices. Finally, in the late 1940's and early 1950's, color television entered the field. Here, as with early black and white, two processes competed. One employed a mechanical scanning disk and a system which was not compatible with existing sets, while the other was entirely electronic and hence compatible. The electronic process won out, and in the United States there are now more than a million color television sets in operation. Yet this is but a fraction of the 55 million black-and-white receivers.

Telegraph, telephone, motion pictures, phonographs, radio, television—these are all part of our daily experience. But what do these things mean and where will they take us? What of computers, artificial satellites to transmit sight and sound around the globe, electronic reproduction of books and newspapers—how can these developments and their refinement in the future change our lives? Are they forces for good or evil, or are they neutral in themselves? An examination of these questions is in order.

118

119

118-121 *The roots of many of the most advanced communications systems of today—high-speed photography, high fidelity amplification, the miracle of electronic computers—lay in the 19th century. On these pages we see several examples which illustrate the slow development of several different media of communications. The magnificent camera (120), all brass and wood, was made by Albert Darrier of Geneva in 1889. It was one of the first to have a sliding plate-holder. The itinerant photographer's box (118) contained collodion with which early film was treated just before exposure, as well as other developing materials. The great horn (119) belonged to an early phonograph public address system. The calculating machine (121) of 1835 was a humble ancestor of today's computers.*

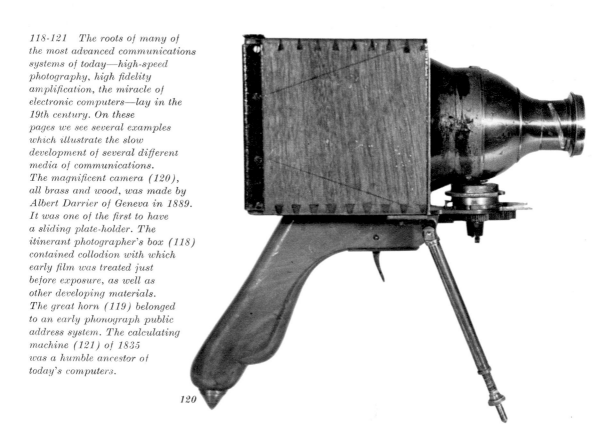

120

121

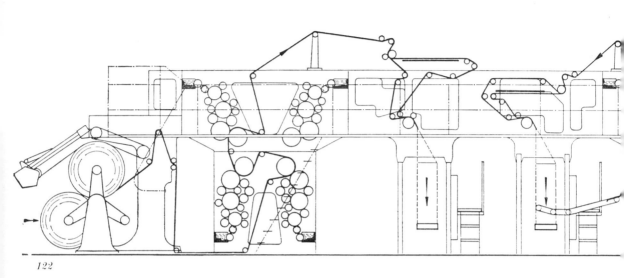

122

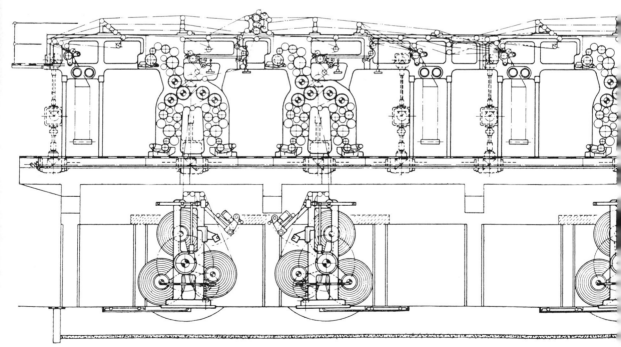

123

122-123 *Two modern European letterpress rotary machines*
(web-fed), high-speed machines used in newspaper printing.
124-125 (Following pages.) Inn sign in Aargau, Switzerland,
an early form of advertising (124). Scandinavian letter box (125).

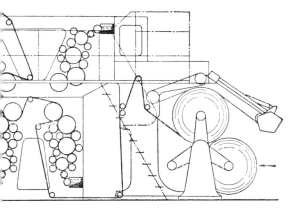

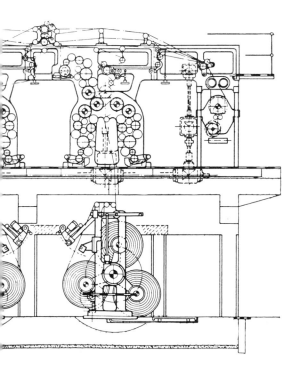

If necessity is the mother of invention, its father is surely previous invention. Each new advance stimulates others in a chain reaction that has become so rapid, at least in the field of communications, that new inventions, as well as refinements of old ones, seem to be announced almost daily. A new age of rapid mass communications is upon us, and if some of its terms are still only dimly understood by most people, others—such as laser, computer, facsimile, television tape, transistor, diode, communications satellite—are already household expressions. Thirty years ago, for example, electronic computers—basically simple machines which can make incredibly rapid electronic decisions—simply did not exist. Today computers perform a variety of tasks in communications as well as in other fields. They track missiles, space vehicles, and ships, keeping a record of where each one is at a given moment; they translate English into Braille, speeding up the production of books for the blind. Soon they will be widely used in libraries to store abstracts of documents and essays, making them instantly available in typescripts to the searching reader; and through a recent I.B.M. invention they will be participating in a fully automatic typesetting system which will be able to set as many as 12,000 justified lines in an hour.

At the heart of computer technology is the transistor—a tiny solid-state electronic component that replaces the vacuum tube. The transistor was invented by three Americans, John Bardeen, Walter Brattain, and William Shockley, and for their discovery they were awarded the Nobel Prize for physics in 1956. The implications of the transistor—and of the

126-137 *Modern communications take many forms—from the giant computers that augment the operations of the human mind, to the tiny transistor radio blaring its tinny music on a beach. But the creations of modern science have not obscured nor impeded one of the oldest forms of communication, the written word. The picture essay on the following pages deliberately ignores the diverse wonders of modern communications to concentrate upon the visible word and symbol as seen by the camera in one of the world's great metropolises. Our pictures show Paris. In London, New York, Rome, or Tokyo the words would be different but the impact would be the same. For the great city is the center and symbol of modern civilization, and in ways too varied to recount, modern civilization is still built around the word.*

more recently developed tunnel diode, another solid-state component—have still to be fully explored, yet these simple devices have already changed much of the technology of mass communications. Without them the space age might still be in the future, for not only are the electronic operations of the transistor and diode much faster than those of the vacuum tube, but as amplifying and transmitting instruments they are much more powerful. In 1961, in the United States alone, 193 million transistors were manufactured.

What happens to so many transistors? Many, of course, go into computers; others are used in space vehicles such as Telstar II, which relays television programs across the oceans, and Mariner II, which has given man much valuable information about earth's closest planetary neighbor, Venus; and many thousands go into radios.

It is in radio that transistors have had the most telling effect, so far as most people are concerned. Gone are the bulky receivers of the past and in their place have come thousands of sleek "pocket-size" portable sets, carried by tribesmen in the jungles of Africa, Bedouins in the Arabian Desert, peasants in the hills of Venezuela, and teenagers on the streets of London, Paris, and New York. The portable transistor radio—which needs no electrical connection—has brought new horizons of entertainment and education to millions who were formerly cut off from the mainstream of civilization. In Venezuela, for example, many peasants are learning to read and write through government-sponsored programs which they pick up on their transistor radios.

But there are only so many wave lengths that can be used for broadcasting purposes. In some industrialized countries the air waves are already becoming cluttered. However, the employment of new types of transmission may overcome the present limitations of radio; and this is becoming a possibility with the invention of the laser, a device applicable to such fields as medicine and astronomy as well as communications. The laser is an instrument for beaming a ray of "coherent" light, which differs from the natural variety in that it contains only one color, whereas light from the sun contains many, each traveling along a different wave length, and causing the light to spread and become diffuse. Laser light, however, remains powerfully intact over great distances (barring the interference of weather). A recent experiment dramatically illustrated this when light from a laser traveled all the way from the earth to the moon. Because it has only one wave length, laser light moves in a steady, narrow beam, and can thus (in theory) be modulated to transmit more information than all the presently available channels of radio. But this is a development for the future.

Also in the future, though technically possible today, lies a device for the photographic transmission of newspapers, books, and letters from central offices to living rooms around the world. Facsimile, as this process is called, has long been used by newspapers and magazines for the rapid transmission of news photographs from one part of the world to another by means of radio waves. An original photograph is scanned by a mechanism containing a light beam and a photoelectric cell, which breaks down the

128

129

130

131

132

133

134

surface into light and dark tones capable of being carried over the air waves. The tones are received by a radio-sensitive, stylus-like instrument which assembles the shadings on chemically treated paper, recreating the original picture. A German, Arthur Korn, was the pathfinder in facsimile. At first he used wires for transmission, and in 1904 succeeded in sending a photo by wire over a distance of 600 miles. Then, fascinated by wireless, he had devised by 1922 a crude means of radiophotography which was the basis of the more sophisticated process used today.

A great step forward was taken in 1947, when the Radio Corporation of America built the Ultrafax, which has proved capable of photographically transmitting a 50,000-word novel over a distance of 3,000 miles in one minute. It draws on radio's great speed, television's ability to break down pages of copy for transmission (at the rate of 30 per second), and the process known as "hot photography," which develops negatives for printing or projecting in a matter of seconds.

Computer typesetting, transistor radios, facsimile, the laser—an insistent question arises: what are we accomplishing for the human race by this ever speedier and more voluminous reproduction and transmission of messages, public and private, around the world, and eventually perhaps to the moon and planets? This is a question for the philosophers; but it is interesting to note that modern communications theory—which is too complex and too technical for a book of this nature—has kept pace with the elaboration of communications technology and indeed, in one well-known case, has arisen from it. Claude Shannon's mathematical theory of information, a basic tool in recent communications studies, was a by-product of his work on the series of inventions which made it possible for AT&T to send five or ten times as many messages over the same cables as before.

Another realm of communications where present applications are but a glimmer of future possibilities is in education. Many schools already employ the services of educational television, and college extension courses are widely given over open channels. But television as it is now used does not really constitute a new method of teaching; it is merely an electronic extension of old methods. Teaching machines, some of which are now in experimental use, do attempt new departures, however, by allowing the student to proceed in the study of a subject at his own pace. Typically, the teaching machine is a device having two screens; on one of which information is given and a question based on it is asked. The student records his answer on the second screen; the response is electronically processed, and if it is incorrect the student is not allowed to proceed until he has mastered the original material and given the right answer. Next more information, based on the original query, is supplied and a new question is asked. Thus the questions move in a logical sequence of small steps, and a pupil may proceed as rapidly or as slowly as his ability and background permit. In a properly "programmed" machine, nothing is left to a chance misunderstanding, for the correct answers can be obtained only through a complete assimilation of the information.

Concurrent with the revolution in mass communications came the development of the modern art of advertising. One cannot call this art (some would say "science") a medium of communication in itself, for it operates through almost all media. Though advertising has almost as many detractors as defenders, any realistic appraisal of Western economics must give it due credit for helping to create the markets that have made the mass production of goods a feasible financial proposition. Advertising made its first great impact in the United States of the 1920's. It was a time of "ballyhoo and bunkum," perfect for the development of the "hard sell." From America its methods spread to Europe, but it was not until after World War II that modern advertising really took hold in the Old World.

To be effective, advertising must operate in an economy rich enough to sustain a high level of consumption among most citizens, and Europe generally did not reach this stage until the 1950's. Europeans have modified American methods, toning them down, often using humor instead of command, and in fact they have taught Americans a few lessons about their own invention. In one area of advertising, poster art, Europe has long led America. An observer in almost any western European city cannot fail to notice the proliferation of posters on walls, kiosks, and fences. They are used to advertise everything from milk to theater to political parties. Often they are crude and propagandistic, but many are utterly charming—a subtle blending of line, color, and lettering into a message intended to tickle the reader into a response.

No mass medium has a monopoly on the functions of communications. The various media interact in such a way that each new development has repercussions on them all. When radio first appeared, many editors considered it a threat to the very existence of the press. As it turned out, radio was no threat at all. It could report the bare bones of the news almost as soon as an event happened, but radio was not geared to the depth analysis and broad coverage that newspapers and news magazines supply. If anything, radio increased newspaper and magazine circulation, for the appetite once whetted by "bare bones" came to demand the richer diet supplied by the printed word.

A far different result came from the impact of television on radio. In order to compete with its sister medium, radio was forced to alter its format. Gone were the comedy shows, thrillers, dramas, and quiz programs, which quickly moved over to the home screen. Radio came to rely more and more on a basic diet of music and news. Yet, thanks in part to the transistor, this formula has been conspicuously successful. In the United States alone there is a radio for almost every man, woman, and child—156 million in all. Of these, over 15 million are equipped to receive frequency-modulation broadcasts, which are carried over ultra-short waves, and are immune to interference from atmospheric disturbances. A development of the mid-1930's that did not come to fruition until after the war, F.M. has proved particularly useful for broadcasting classical music, thanks to its great tonal fidelity. So effective has it been in this field that it has precipitated a boom in sales of classical records, and this in turn has led to an increased

*138 Antennas of all kinds are vitally
important in the massive network of
electronic communications of the present
day. Used to detect enemy planes and
missiles, antennas placed along
the frontiers protect a country from
surprise attack. Other antennas play
a major role in radio and television
communications while still others are
widely used in tracking and guiding
space probes and satellites.*
*139 Model of the Telstar satellite,
launched by the United States in 1962.
By means of this satellite, telephone
and television communications were
exchanged between the United States
and Europe. The Japanese are
preparing a relay station from which,
via such satellites, they may broadcast the 1964
Olympic Games.*

139

demand for F.M. receivers and wider broad-casting facilities. The new development of "multiplex," a system for stereophonic broadcasting over F.M., promises to improve the quality of music reception in the home, giving the listener the illusion of being in a concert hall. In time this too will probably be reflected in increased sales of stereophonic phonographs and records.

If television has changed radio, its impact on the cinema has been revolutionary. For over 40 years the motion picture had the field of visual entertainment almost to itself. This period has often been called the "golden age" of cinema, and in many ways it was. Great directors like D. W. Griffith, Charles Chaplin, René Clair, Alfred Hitchcock, Sergei M. Eisenstein, and Orson Welles worked miracles on celluloid. With films like *The Birth of a Nation*, *Under the Roofs of Paris*, *The Gold Rush*, *The Thirty-Nine Steps*, *Alexander Nevsky*, and *Citizen Kane* they turned the motion picture into one of the most potent entertainment, educational, and propaganda media of all time. Other directors brought the stylized "Western" into its own as almost an art form in itself. By the time television became a reality, tens of millions of people were streaming into motion-picture theaters every week. The motion picture industry, and particularly Hollywood, had come to regard this situation as an almost unchangeable fact of life. Television quickly destroyed this illusion and Hollywood soon found itself in a desperately competitive position.

Hollywood's reaction to this disaster took many forms. Wide screens, stereophonic sound, three-dimensional viewing, and even motion pictures that emitted odors were results of this struggle. Some motion picture companies took to the making of huge spectacles like *Cleopatra*, an area in which television could hardly compete, while others took the easy way out by making serials for television. A more hopeful reaction lay in the making of better films. A new generation of directors, many of them fresh from television, came to Hollywood and dismantled one of the most cherished beliefs of the magnates, that thought-provoking motion pictures would not sell. Directors like Elia Kazan and John Frankenheimer have narrowed the gap between the "art film," aimed at a small audience of intellectuals, and the general run of motion pictures. At the same time, the decline of Hollywood as the world's film capital was matched by the rise of the motion picture industries of Britain, France, Italy, India, Japan, and Sweden, which have often pointed the way for Hollywood in the development of cinema as a serious entertainment and art form.

Ever since the advent of electronic communications, prophets of doom have predicted the ultimate demise of the written word. Certainly the word is more than ever with us in the form of road signs, maps, schedules, telephone directories, advertisements, and the like. And in the form of mass circulation magazines and newspapers. Recently it was estimated that over 90 per cent of Britain's adult population reads at least one newspaper a day. In the United States the combined circulation of the daily press stands at almost 59 million. Books, too, seem to have thrived in this era. More than 800 million volumes are printed every year in the United States alone; in 1961 about 15,000

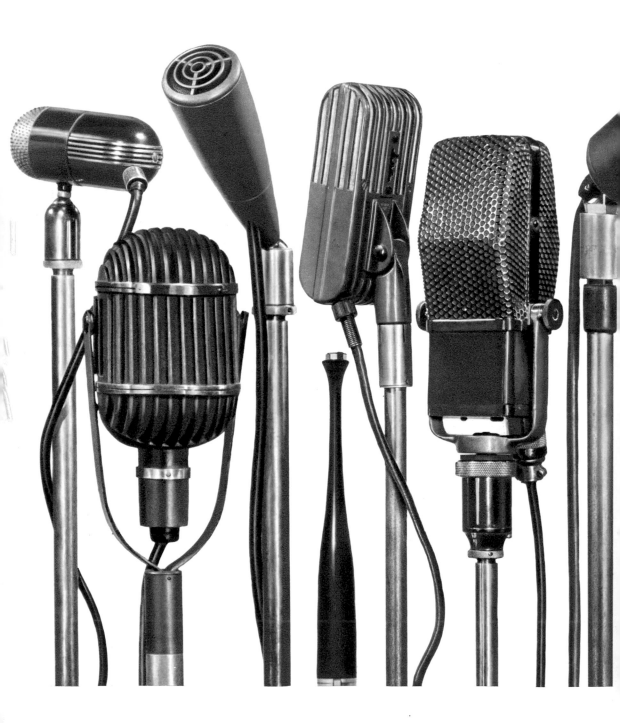

140 *Various types of microphones used by the Columbia Broadcasting System, an American radio-TV network. At the end of the 19th century, basing his work on the earlier discoveries and experiments of James Clerk Maxwell and Heinrich Hertz, Guglielmo Marconi was able to send wireless messages in Morse code. The first broadcast of the human voice took place in 1906, and a year later Lee De Forest invented the "audion," or three element vacuum tube, which is the basis not only of radio but of all electronics. Wireless communication was important during World War I, but only as wireless telegraphy, for it was not until after the war that commercial wireless, or radio, became an entertainment medium.*

141 *A view of New York rooftops shows how avidly the public has taken to television in the United States. Europe is rapidly catching up and soon this scene will be typical of any large city in the world. As an industry, as a leading entertainment medium, as a miracle of electronic engineering, television dates only from the years after World War II. The first attempts to send images by wire, however, took place a century ago, and after that there were repeated efforts by many inventors to create a non-electronic television system. Not until 1920 did the modern television system begin to emerge. In 1923 pictures of the American President Harding were successfully transmitted from Washington to Baltimore by the American TV pioneer, Charles Francis Jenkins.*

new titles were published. Though Europeans have long been familiar with the paperback book—and it is no recent development in America either—the mass distribution of inexpensive paperbacks in the United States is a phenomenon of the postwar years. The bulk of the 300 million sold yearly are of course cheap thrillers and westerns, but thousands are classics and other serious works. New distribution channels for paperbacks as well as other books —including newspaper stands, mail order solicitation, supermarkets, and pharmacies—have also augmented the quantity, and sometimes even the quality, of the books sold in America.

Yet these statistics on the sale of books, as well as of newspapers and magazines, must be judged against the enormous growth in the world's population, against the increase in expendable wealth, against the rising number of reasonably educated people, and similar factors. In this light it will be seen perhaps that the printed word is barely holding its own against the mass media, and may even be slipping a bit. Ominously, in the United States, where the mass media are most highly developed, fewer books are sold or read per capita than in Europe. On the other hand, are the mass media as culturally degrading as this implies? Perhaps, in the main, they are at present; but no medium of communications stands still; there is room for change, for growth. It is possible to foresee the day when all the media of communication, from books through television to computers and teaching machines will harmoniously combine to instruct as well as to entertain the broad mass of citizens around the world.

chronology

20,000 *Approximate date of the earliest prehistoric cave paintings, found in north-eastern Spain. Other cave paintings have been discovered in southwestern France, in northern Europe, around the eastern Mediterranean, and in the Sahara.*

8000 *Pebbles painted with geometric symbols, dating from this period, have been found at Mas d'Azil, France.*

3500 *The Sumerians develop a type of pictographic writing which eventually evolves into cuneiform.*

3100 *Date of the earliest known examples of Egyptian hieroglyphic writing.*

2500 *The Egyptians begin to use a new writing material, papyrus, which they make from stems of reeds. The cursive hieratic script, later used only for religious writings, is developed at about the same time and is mostly written on papyrus.*

1800 *Height of Babylonian culture. An extensive literature in cuneiform writing is recorded on clay tablets, and the famous law code of Hammurabi is inscribed on a stele.*

1800- *The peoples of Syria-*
1600 *Palestine develop the first real alphabet, later transmitted by the Phoenicians to the Greeks in the tenth century B.C.*

1700- *The Minoans of Crete, who*
1450 *developed a very advanced civilization, use two types of script, so-called linear A and B.*

1580- *During the 18th*
1350 *Dynasty in Egypt a papyrus known as "The Book of the Dead" is written. This is considered to be the world's first book as it is the oldest surviving papyrus of any length.*

800 *Approximate date of the "Illiad" and the "Odyssey," epics presumably recounted by the Greek poet Homer.*

800 *The Etruscans adopt the alphabet from the Greeks, later passing it on to the Romans.*

700 *Emergence of the demotic script in Egypt, the form used for non-official, non-religious writing on papyrus.*

700 *The Persians take over the cuneiform system of writing, adapting it to their Indo-European language, and coming close to the development of an alphabet.*

540 *Foundation of what may have been the first public library, by Pisistratus, in Athens.*

350 *All the Greek states adopt a 24-letter alphabet.*

04- **0**	During the zenith of the Alexandrian culture, the two royal libraries contain some 490,000 scrolls.
07	Foundation of the guild of scribes, in Rome.
00- **50**	Parchment, a new writing material made from the skins of animals, is perfected in Pergamum, an ancient Greek state.
31	The Roman "acta diurna," official announcements posted in public places, are the forerunners of the newspaper.
00	The Romans, in particular the Sosii brothers, having worked up an efficient system of publishing, copy and sell manuscript books, or rolls, made of the new parchment. Some copyright laws, censorship, and a system of public libraries also exist in Roman times.
00	The Roman alphabet attains its final 23-letter form.
59	Julius Caesar orders the publication of the "acta senatus," the debates of the senate. Caesar also orders the preparation of a map of the Empire.

A.D.

48	Invading Alexandria, Roman soldiers sack the famous libraries.
105	Ts'ai Lun of China perfects a method of making paper from inexpensive fibers.
150	Parchment is for the first time folded into pages to make books, rather than being rolled up into scrolls.
391	During the reign of the zealous Christian convert, Emperor Theodosius I, the Romans carry further the destruction of the Alexandrian libraries.
400- **1400**	The Dark Ages in Europe after the fall of the Roman Empire. Throughout this period the monasteries of the Catholic Church are the sole centers of learning. Monks, working in special rooms called "scriptoria," become expert at copying and illuminating manuscripts.
600	The Chinese art of paper-making spreads to Japan and Korea and westward to Persia.
676	In capturing Samarkand in eastern Persia, the Arabs fall heir to many ideas and inventions which had seeped west from China, including papermaking. Not until the thirteenth century, however, was this art passed on to Europe.
868	The "Diamond Sutra," now at the British Museum, is the first complete printed book.

900	During the height of the Carolingian-Frankish Empire, present-day writing takes its form—two offshoots being the gothic and the italic styles of writing.
900	Date of the Irish "Book of Kells," a masterpiece of illumination.
1034	In China, Pi Sheng invents movable type made of firebaked clay.
1167	Foundation of Oxford University in England.
1200	Charter of the University of Paris.
1204	Foundation of the University of Vicenza.
1221	Movable type made of wood appears in China.
1373	Charles V opens what is now the National Library in Paris (it now has more than four million books).
1385	Heidelberg University is founded.
1390	In Korea, the Emperor Tsai-Tung orders bronze type for printing.
1418	Xylography, or the art of engraving on wood and printing from these engravings, appears in Europe.
1445	During the Ming Dynasty, the Chinese begin to use copper type in printing.
1450	Johann Gutenberg of Mainz invents both movable type and the press, thus founding printing in Europe.
1456	Gutenberg's Bible is the first book printed from movable type in the West.
1476	William Caxton sets up a printing press in England, and a year later publishes the first book printed in that country. Most of Caxton's books are printed in English, whereas all European countries with the exception of Spain do three-quarters of their printing in Latin. After 1500 however, printing in the vernacular gains in importance.
1501	Aldus Manutius, printer of Venice and originator of the "pocket edition," adopts the italic type designed by Francesco Griffo of Bologna. The first book had been printed in gothic type, or "black letter," but roman or italic type was largely to replace this.
1502	Foundation of the renowned printing house of the Estienne family, in France.
1500- **1550**	The major trading companies of Europe circulate hand-written "newsletters," fore-runners of the newspaper.
1513	Appearance of the first English "newsbook," which tells the story of the Battle of Flodden Field.
1546	French printer Etienne Dolet is burned at the stake

as a heretic, along with
his books.

1582 *Pope Gregory XIII introduces
the Gregorian Calendar, still
in use today.*

1590 *Publication of J. B. Porta's
"Natural Magic," containing
a description of the camera
obscura.*

1602 *John Willis publishes a
treatise on shorthand
writing.*

1609 *One of the first weekly
newspapers to be regularly
published appears in
Strasbourg.*

1620 *Publication of the "Nieuwe
Tijdinghen," a Belgian
news sheet, which is the first
to contain illustrations.*

1631 *Théophraste Renaudot begins
publication of "La Gazette
de France," first major
French periodical.*

1640 *Cardinal Richelieu founds
the royal printing works
in France.*

1644 *Publication of Milton's
"Areopagitica," a plea for
freedom of expression.*

1653 *Opening of a public library
in Boston.*

1662 *There are 60 publishers in
London at this time.*

1667 *English physicist Robert
Hooke experiments with
the use of taut strings for
the transmission of sound.*

1672 *Foundation of the "Mercure
Galant," (now known as
the "Mercure de France"),
one of the first feature
periodicals.*

1690 *Appearance of the Boston
"Publick Occurrences,"
first newspaper of the
American colonies,
suppressed after one issue.*

1695 *Partial freeing of the press
in England through the
abolition of the Licensing
Act by Parliament.*

1702 *Appearance of the "Daily
Courant," first of the daily
newspapers, in London,
March 1.*

1709 *Passage of the Copyright
Act in England, first
modern copyright law.*

1725 *Scotsman William Ged
invents stereotypy, which
enables printers to make
molds of printed surfaces so
that metal plates for future
editions can be cast from
the original mold.*

1734 *New York newspaper
publisher John Peter Zenger
is acquitted of a libel charge.
This establishes in the British
colonies that truth is a
defense against libel
accusation.*

1750 *Britisher John Baskerville,
inventor of a typeface still
popular today, develops a
fine quality paper which he
calls vellum. Baskerville also
improves printers' ink.*

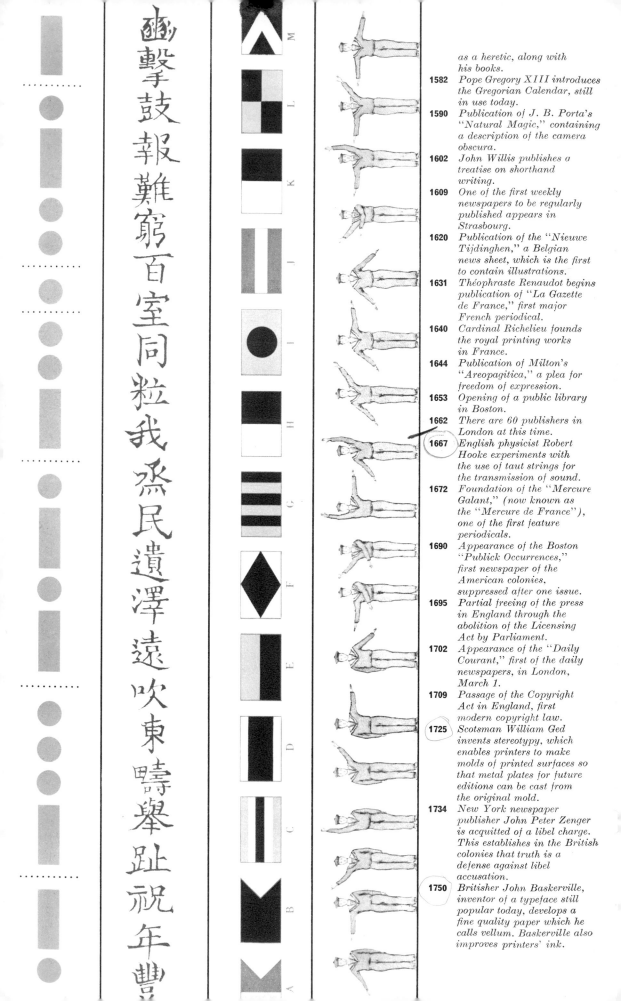

776	Virginia Bill of Rights singles out the press as the "bulwark of liberty."
785	Appearance of the first number of John Walter's "Daily Universal Register," (which three years later becomes the London "Times"), January 1.
791	First amendment of the United States Constitution guarantees freedom of the press.
794	Using the optical telegraph invented by Claude Chappe, the French construct a system of telegraph stations connecting Paris and Lille.
796-799	Bavarian Alois Senefelder perfects his invention, lithography.
799	Discovery of the Rosetta Stone, key to the decipherment of Egyptian hieroglyphics.
803	A process for the continuous manufacture of paper is used for the first time, in England.
814	The London "Times" operates the first steam-powered cylindrical press, invented by the German Friedrich König. It produces 1,100 news sheets per hour.
822	Frenchman Nicéphore Niepce makes the first photograph. Seven years later he begins to work in association with Jacques Daguerre.
822	French scholar Jean-François Champollion, using the Rosetta Stone, deciphers Egyptian hieroglyphics.
835	James Gordon Bennett founds the New York "Herald."
837	Daguerre invents a system of developing images on metal plates coated with silver oxide.
839	Journals appear with photographs in Europe, thanks to Daguerre's new process.
840	Introduction of a method of making paper from wood pulp, in Germany.
841	Fox Talbot patents the calotype, or negative-positive process for photography.
841	Horace Greeley founds the New York "Tribune," which becomes the "Herald Tribune" after a 1924 merger.
844	The Chappe telegraph network in France connects 29 cities through 500 stations.
845-846	Richard March Hoe perfects his rotary press, capable of producing 8,000 papers an hour, in Philadelphia.
846	Henry C. Rawlinson publishes his work on the cuneiform inscriptions of the Behistun Rock, found in Persia.
848	A group of New York newspapers form an association or news agency later called the Associated Press.

1850	Laying of the first international telegraph cable, between Calais and Dover.
1851	Founding of the New York "Daily Times," called "The New York Times" after 1857.
1851	Paul Julius Reuter organizes his commercial wire service.
1858	Laying of the first transatlantic telegraph cable, between Ireland and Newfoundland. Corrosion soon causes the cable to break.
1861	The "Daily Telegraph" initiates the popular press in England.
1863	The French popular press begins with publication of "Le Petit Journal."
1865	An improved model of Johann Philipp Reis's 1861 telephone allegedly transmits intelligible speech.
1865	James Clerk Maxwell publishes his electromagnetic theory of light.
1866	Another transatlantic cable is laid, this one totally successful.
1870	Adoption of a compulsory education law in England which, with the act of 1890 establishing free elementary education, marks a great step forward in the eradication of illiteracy.
1875	Invention of heliogravure, a process of photoengraving, by Karl Klietsch.
1876	Alexander Graham Bell invents the telephone.
1878	Thomas A. Edison develops a cylindrical phonograph.
1880	Johann Martin Schleyer invents "Volapük" in an attempt to create a universal language.
1882	France institutes compulsory primary education.
1883	Joseph Pulitzer buys the New York "World."
1884	George Eastman invents the roll film.
1884	Paul Nipkow works out a mechanical scanning disk, used in early television research.
1885	William Randolph Hearst buys the New York "Journal."
1885	The first linotype machine is patented by American Ottmar Mergenthaler.
1886	Signing of the International Copyright Convention, a step towards reciprocity of rights.
1887	Tolbert Lanston invents the monotype machine.
1887	Dr. L. Zamenhof develops "Esperanto," most successful of the attempts to create an artificial universal language.
1887	Heinrich Hertz, German physicist, experimentally verifies Maxwell's theories, leading toward wireless and radio.

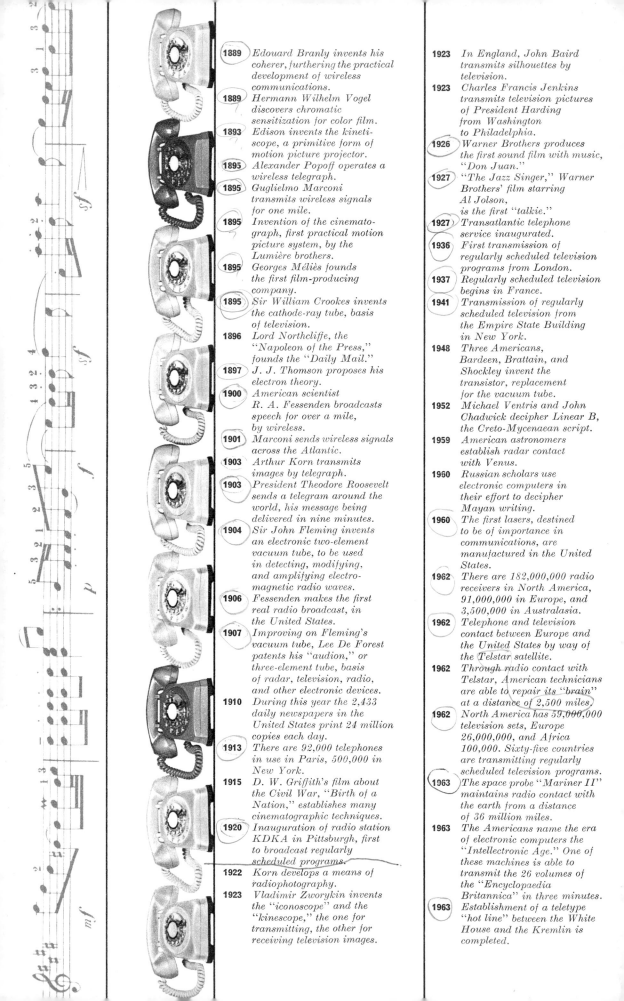

1889 Edouard Branly invents his coherer, furthering the practical development of wireless communications.

1889 Hermann Wilhelm Vogel discovers chromatic sensitization for color film.

1893 Edison invents the kinetiscope, a primitive form of motion picture projector.

1895 Alexander Popoff operates a wireless telegraph.

1895 Guglielmo Marconi transmits wireless signals for one mile.

1895 Invention of the cinematograph, first practical motion picture system, by the Lumière brothers.

1895 Georges Méliès founds the first film-producing company.

1895 Sir William Crookes invents the cathode-ray tube, basis of television.

1896 Lord Northcliffe, the "Napoleon of the Press," founds the "Daily Mail."

1897 J. J. Thomson proposes his electron theory.

1900 American scientist R. A. Fessenden broadcasts speech for over a mile, by wireless.

1901 Marconi sends wireless signals across the Atlantic.

1903 Arthur Korn transmits images by telegraph.

1903 President Theodore Roosevelt sends a telegram around the world, his message being delivered in nine minutes.

1904 Sir John Fleming invents an electronic two-element vacuum tube, to be used in detecting, modifying, and amplifying electromagnetic radio waves.

1906 Fessenden makes the first real radio broadcast, in the United States.

1907 Improving on Fleming's vacuum tube, Lee De Forest patents his "audion," or three-element tube, basis of radar, television, radio, and other electronic devices.

1910 During this year the 2,433 daily newspapers in the United States print 24 million copies each day.

1913 There are 92,000 telephones in use in Paris, 500,000 in New York.

1915 D. W. Griffith's film about the Civil War, "Birth of a Nation," establishes many cinematographic techniques.

1920 Inauguration of radio station KDKA in Pittsburgh, first to broadcast regularly scheduled programs.

1922 Korn develops a means of radiophotography.

1923 Vladimir Zworykin invents the "iconoscope" and the "kinescope," the one for transmitting, the other for receiving television images.

1923 In England, John Baird transmits silhouettes by television.

1923 Charles Francis Jenkins transmits television pictures of President Harding from Washington to Philadelphia.

1926 Warner Brothers produces the first sound film with music, "Don Juan."

1927 "The Jazz Singer," Warner Brothers' film starring Al Jolson, is the first "talkie."

1927 Transatlantic telephone service inaugurated.

1936 First transmission of regularly scheduled television programs from London.

1937 Regularly scheduled television begins in France.

1941 Transmission of regularly scheduled television from the Empire State Building in New York.

1948 Three Americans, Bardeen, Brattain, and Shockley invent the transistor, replacement for the vacuum tube.

1952 Michael Ventris and John Chadwick decipher Linear B, the Creto-Mycenaean script.

1959 American astronomers establish radar contact with Venus.

1960 Russian scholars use electronic computers in their effort to decipher Mayan writing.

1960 The first lasers, destined to be of importance in communications, are manufactured in the United States.

1962 There are 182,000,000 radio receivers in North America, 91,000,000 in Europe, and 3,500,000 in Australasia.

1962 Telephone and television contact between Europe and the United States by way of the Telstar satellite.

1962 Through radio contact with Telstar, American technicians are able to repair its "brain" at a distance of 2,500 miles.

1962 North America has 59,000,000 television sets, Europe 26,000,000, and Africa 100,000. Sixty-five countries are transmitting regularly scheduled television programs.

1963 The space probe "Mariner II" maintains radio contact with the earth from a distance of 36 million miles.

1963 The Americans name the era of electronic computers the "Intellectronic Age." One of these machines is able to transmit the 26 volumes of the "Encyclopaedia Britannica" in three minutes.

1963 Establishment of a teletype "hot line" between the White House and the Kremlin is completed.

Among those who have assisted in the preparation of this book grateful acknowledgment must be made to Courtlandt Canby, General Editor, Helen Muller, Suzanne Patrick, and Eric Tschumi of the ENI staff, as well as to Dean Gilbert Seldes of the Annenberg School of Communications, who read the manuscript with care.

Nicolas Bouvier and Roger-Jean Ségalat, Picture Research.

credits

"Album Gutenberg," 1840 : 48
"Betles Enseignes de Suisse," René Creux, 1962 : 124
Bettmann Archive, New York : 98
Bibliothèque d'Art et d'Archéologie, Geneva : 5-8, 53, 55, 57, 59-63
Bibliothèque de Genève : 12, 16, 18, 24, 27, 44, 82
Bibliothèque Nationale, Paris : frontispiece, 1-3, 9-11, 17, 19, 28-30, 32-43, 45, 47, 52, 54, 56, 58, 64-71, 79, 80
Brassaï, Paris : 129, 132, 135
CBS Radio, New York : 140
Collection Nicolas Bouvier : 115, 116
Collection Gaston Burnand : 46
Collection Hugues Fontanet : 100, 107-110, 113
Collection Dr. Liebeskind : 103-106, 111, 112, 114
Collection Musée de l'Homme, Paris : 13, 14, 26
Collection George Sirot : 96
Deutsches Museum, Munich : 21, 85, 86, 93, 101
Free Lance Photographers Guild, New York : 15, 95, Photo Al Naidoff 141
General Dynamics (Stromberg-Carlson), New York : 92, 94
Giraudon, Paris : 20, 22, 25, 49-51, 83, 84, 89
Kennedy Antenna Division, Electronic Specialty Co., USA : 138
"La Nature," 1886 : 102
"L'Encyclopédie," Diderot, 1751 : 31, 72-75, 77
M.A.N., Augsburg : 122
"Méliès," Lo Duca and Maurice Bessy, Ed. J.-J. Pauvert : 99
Mission H. Lhote, Ed. Arthaud, Paris : 4
Musée des Arts et Métiers, Paris : 88, 90, 118-121
Musée d'Histoire de l'Education, Paris : 78
Musée du Louvre, Paris : 23
Musée Postal, Paris : 81, 117
Photo David Kronig, Geneva : 126, 130, 131, 133, 134, 137
Rapho, Paris : IFOT—Photo Parbst 125, Photo Robert Doisneau 127, 128, 136
UNESCO, Paris : Photo David Seymour 142
USIS, Paris : 91, 139
Viollet, Paris : 76, 87, 97
Wifag, Bern : 123

Chronology

Asile des Aveugles, Geneva : 9
Collection Erik Nitsche : 2-4, 6, 10
Eric Tschumi : 5, 7
General Dynamics (Stromberg-Carlson), New York : 12
IBM : 13
"Larousse du XXᵉ siècle," : 8
"L'Illustration" 1891 : 14
"Writing," David Diringer, 1962 : 1

. . . . *Je* . . . .

. . . . *v* . . . .

. . . . *ous* . . . . *ai* . . . .

. . . . *me* . . . . .

Printed in Switzerland